DOOMSDAY BUNKER BOOK

Underground Edition

By Ben Jakob

Cover Design by The Pro Doodler

DOOMSDAY BUNKER BOOK

Your Complete Guide to Designing, Surviving and Living in an Underground Concrete Bunker, and for When TSHTF

By Ben Jakob
www.doomsdaybunkerbook.com

DISCLAIMER

www.doomsdaybunkerbook.com
doomsdaybunkerbook@gmail.com

Ordering Information:
Quantity sales. Special discounts are available on quantity purchases by corporations, associations, and others. For details, contact the publisher at the above address.

Printed in the United States of America

First Edition

14 13 12 11 10 / 10 9 8 7 6 5 4 3 2 1

ISBN #978-0-9905891-0-5

Doomsday Bunker Book

Underground Edition

Your Complete Guide to Designing, Surviving and Living in a Concrete Bunker

Ben Jakob

DISCLAIMER

THIS book is for entertainment purposes only and is intended to provide information on designing, building and living in an underground concrete bunker or for a doomsday situation. It is sold with the understanding the publisher nor the author are engaged in rendering legal, accounting, medical, mechanical or other professional services. If legal or other expert assistance is required, the services of a competent professional should be sought.

The information contained in Doomsday Bunker Book are recommendations by the author, and reading this book does not guarantee your results will be the same as his.

The material herein includes information, products and services by third parties. These do not necessarily mirror the opinions of the author, and all third party materials comprise the opinions of their respective owners.

The publication of such third party materials does not constitute the author's guarantee of any information, opinion, products or services from the third party material.

It is not the purpose of this book to be comprehensive and reprint all the information otherwise available to the public, but instead to complement, amplify and supplement other texts. You are urged to read all available material, learn as much as possible, and tailor the information to your individual needs.

Every effort has been made to make this book as complete and as accurate as possible. However, there may be mistakes, both typographical and in content. Therefore, this text should be used only as a general guide and not as the ultimate source for concrete bunker information. Furthermore, this book contains information on concrete bunker design and living that is current only up to the printing date. The purpose of this manual is to educate and entertain. The author shall have neither liability nor responsibility to any person or entity with respect to any loss or damage caused, or alleged to have been caused, directly or indirectly, by the information contained in this book.

If you do not wish to be bound by the above, you may return this book within fourteen days of purchase to the publisher for a full refund.

Sorry, I have to throw in that legaleze.

TABLE OF CONTENTS

TABLE OF CONTENTS

TABLE OF CONTENTS

TABLE OF CONTENTS

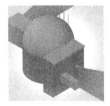

INTRODUCTION

WE all have heard of people talking about a doomsday, or watched the TV show Doomsday Preppers. We have heard people called "Preppers", or "What Iffers". People have been talking about some sort of "End of the World" scenario, for decades. Even the United States government has many bunkers around the country, some of which have been bought by ordinary citizens and even preppers. Some of us are concerned something may happen sooner rather than later. I have heard more and more people talking about the possibility of an imminent disaster. Some people worry about different possible scenarios. For example; economic collapse, societal collapse, civil unrest, electromagnetic pulse, weather destruction, war, fire, nuclear attacks, terrorist attacks, fuel shortages, pandemics, geomagnetic reversal, etc. Sixty-one percent of Americans believe some sort of "doomsday" will happen within the next twenty years.

Many people are preparing for the scenarios of which they are concerned. It is estimated in the United States of America, approximately ten percent of the population are preppers to one degree or another. No one knows if or when, one or more problems will occur. There is no way to predict a specific occurrence or time factor, and my crystal ball broke, so I cannot help with your prognostication. The best we can do is to prepare for any eventuality. This is why I personally (and many others) believe an underground concrete bunker is the best idea. As I will explain, this bunker will give you the best protection possible for the most scenarios.

One need not be a conspiracy theorist to be concerned. People may think "doomsday preppers", or "what ifers", as we are often called, are "nut jobs." However, when TSHTF, we will be the ones who others will come to, since we will be prepared.

Some of the problems I have seen with bunker designs are:

- There is not enough food storage
- There is not enough water storage
- The bunker is not deep enough underground to protect from radiation or chemical contamination
- The bunker is not designed to be able to withstand the amount of pressure from the tonnage of dirt above
- The air circulation is not adequate
- The air is not adequately filtered for NBC (Nuclear, Biological, Chemical) contamination
- The water is not sufficiently filtered
- There are no accommodations for pets.
- There is no accommodation (or insufficient accommodation) for waste and elimination.
- Bunkers are too crowded and claustrophobic for long term occupancy.
- Security is woefully inadequate.
- Security plans are unrealistic
- There is no adequate plan for replenishing the water
- There is no adequate plan for replenishing the food
- No mental diversion or entertainment planned

- Steel shipping containers do not supply the protection needed, nor are they able to be buried deep enough underground for adequate protection.
- There is no escape plan
- There is no second exit
- What about electricity?
- No plan for backups
- No bug-out kits prepared
- No drills planned
- Occupants are not knowledgeable about nuclear protection.

In my design, I have tried to counter these challenges and make a bunker that is workable, livable for the long term, comfortable and realistic.

My biggest challenge is I do not yet have the free cash to be able to do what I want and complete the bunker I have delineated in this book. I want to be clear upfront with you, I have not actually finished building the bunker I describe, however, I am working toward this goal and I have already started the process. I am not an engineer, however I have consulted with several engineers (structural, mechanical, and architectural) for this project. I am a professional architectural and mechanical draftsman, and researcher by trade and education, and have put my skills and education to work to prepare this book. I want to share with you the research I have done, so you will not have to do it yourself. This book is the design I am using to make my own bunker. At the time of this writing, I am well on my way building my bunker. In fact, by the time you read this book, I hope to have my bunker built. I make no warrantees, implicit or implied by this book. You are following my advice at your own risk. (Sorry, I have to throw in that legaleze.)

I am giving you many links to other websites for reference. I receive no compensation or kickback in any way for this. I have included these links to help in your planning and preparation with making your own underground bunker and shelter.

There are going to be several suggestions specific to Jews. I will indicate such at the appropriate places. Please contact your orthodox rabbi for confirmation and explanation on any Jewish law.

As a side note, I live in the United States of America, so the measurements herein are all imperial. However, since this book is also being sold internationally, I will put metric measurements in {} wherever possible. Please keep in mind since I am unfamiliar with international standard sizes, I am just approximating.

CHARTS

UNFORTUNATELY, DUE TO THE SIZE restrictions in printing a book of this type, you will notice some charts in this book do not look great. However, I still want to share with you the information herein. To wit, I have put all the necessary charts on the website www.doomsdaybunkerbook.com. Of course, there is no additional charge for the charts found in this book.

OPTIONAL EXTRAS

THE PRICE YOU PAID FOR this book is complete in that we are finished financially. However, if you would like to enhance your knowledge and be better prepared, I have a few optional extras available for purchase from the website. Since you purchased the "Doomsday Bunker Book", when you purchase any of the extras, you receive a substantial discount. Please feel free to contact me with any questions. The prices for the optional extras are mentioned on the website. As time goes on, I will have additional supplements on the website some for free and some for a nominal fee.

- This book is available in both eBook and paperback.
- In this book, I have included several sketches of the main parts of the bunker. There are also several tables and charts to help you along. Please refer to them often as you read this book.
- If you would like more detailed drawings of the bunker than what is included in this book, please see the website for pricing.
- Being that I am an architectural and mechanical draftsman by trade, if you would like my assistance in designing a bunker for your specific size and needs, I will be happy to do so. Please contact me for a price quote.
- You will notice throughout this book I make references to "storage areas". I have spent considerable time and effort delving into where I think certain things should go in the bunker. I do this to make your life in the bunker more convenient. The list would include what goes in which storage areas and several drawings showing exactly where the storage areas are located. Please see the website for pricing.
- I have also designed an aboveground bunker. Please see the website for pricing for either the book or the eBook.
- I have a number of great recipes that will be great for someone living in a bunker, especially in a time of SHTF. There are over 200 recipes in the Recipe eBook. It comes with a free eBook Kitchen Manual. Please see the website for pricing.
- We have a Doomsday Bunker Book club. Since you bought one of our products (this book) you are eligible to join at no charge. You will have access to a special Skype name that you may call me with questions about your bunker. There will also be new articles posted exclusively for club members, and much more. Terms are posted on the website.

- We have a newsletter available for free subscription.
- There are other articles and tips on the website.

Please check my website often as I will be making updates regularly. www.doomsdaybunkerbook.com.

Please also join our Facebook page
https://www.facebook.com/groups/241463699375800/

TIPS

BEFORE we get started, I want to share with you some tips to help make your life easier and more comfortable.

Always remember that, "One is none and two is one". Meaning, always have a backup. This is essential. What I have listed herein does not include backups unless otherwise stated.

Since you will want to live off the grid as much as possible and not have anyone know your exact address, I suggest you get a post office box for mail. You will still have to pay your taxes; however, you are less likely to be found by the average person. In no way am I advocating breaking any law, as law enforcement will easily find you. Do NOT break any laws. No one should ever know the exact location of your bunker - not even family.

www.cheaperthandirt.com is a good resource.

Learn how to weld, and purchase welding equipment. http://www.millerwelds.com/ http://www.instructables.com/id/How-to-Weld---MIG-Welding/step2/How-the-Machine-Works/

LDS Prepper on YouTube
desertsun02 on You Tube

I will be including some information that is not specifically germane to living in a bunker, however it is good to know for anyone living when TSHTF.

You should start collecting fire starters. Also combustibles: Dryer lint, crayons, pine needles, toilet paper tubes, paper towel tubes, commercial fire starters, flint, matches, candles, etc.

Do not ignore your spiritual health.

Get a Ham radio (Amateur Radio) license and a 2 meter radio. You will want an antenna on the surface and a cable leading down to the bunker in the command center.

WEBSITES

THE following chart is a list of all the websites I mention in this book. I put together this list in order to make it more convenient for you.

- http://www.doomsdaybunkerbook.com
- http://www.theprodoodler.com
- http://www.yourkosherchef.com
- http://4volt.com/Blog/archive/2009/06/09/diy-3-stage-air-filter.aspx
- http://www.allselfsustained.com/generate-electricity-from-waste/
- http://www.amazon.com/gp/product/B003FWNWWI/ref=as_li_ss_tl?ie=UTF8&camp=1789&creative=390957&creativeASIN=B003FWNWWI&linkCode=as2&tag=yt0c-20
- http://www.amazon.com/gp/product/B002DTV172/ref=as_li_ss_tl?ie=UTF8&camp=1789&creative=390957&creativeASIN=B002DTV172&linkCode=as2&tag=yt0c-20
- http://www.amazon.com/gp/product/B003Z3EZ1O/ref=as_li_ss_tl?ie=UTF8&camp=1789&creative=390957&creativeASIN=B003Z3EZ1O&linkCode=as2&tag=yt0c-20

- http://www.amazon.com/gp/product/B000BPTUFK/ref=as_li_ss_tl?ie=UTF8&camp=1789&creative=390957&creativeASIN=B000BPTUFK&linkCode=as2&tag=yt0c-20
- http://www.amazon.com/gp/product/B003HGHQT2/ref=as_li_ss_tl?ie=UTF8&camp=1789&creative=390957&creativeASIN=B003HGHQT2&linkCode=as2&tag=yt0c-20
- http://www.amazon.com/mn/search/?_encoding=UTF8&camp=1789&creative=390957&field-keywords=anl%20fuse&linkCode=ur2&sprefix=anl%2Caps%2C175&tag=yt0c-20&url=search-alias%3Daps
- http://www.amazon.com/First-Alert-RD1-Radon-Test/dp/B00002N83E/ref=sr_1_1/184-7040453-7397635?ie=UTF8&qid=1396155592&sr=8-1&keywords=radon+testing+kit
- http://www.amazon.com/gp/product/B005FD7Z82/ref=as_li_qf_sp_asin_il_tl?ie=UTF8&camp=1789&creative=9325&creativeASIN=B005FD7Z82&linkCode=as2&tag=prepperswor05-20&linkId=HAH5KI62OIV4PZHG
- http://www.amazon.com/gp/product/B004NJS7VS/ref=as_li_ss_tl?ie=UTF8&tag=yt0c-20&linkCode=as2&camp=1789&creative=390957&creativeASIN=B004NJS7VS
- http://www.amazon.com/MTM-Forest-Green-Caliber-Storage/dp/B003TNV46O/ref=br_lf_m_1001140791_1_10_img/186-0298701-9219901?_encoding=UTF8&s=sporting-goods&pf_rd_m=ATVPDKIKX0DER&pf_rd_s=center-3&pf_rd_r=01ZM6W4225STWHM8HZAV&pf_rd_t=1401&pf_rd_p=1635249502&pf_rd_i=1001140791
- http://www.amazon.com/Grape-Solar-GS-P-280-Fab1-280-Watt-Polycrystalline/dp/B00635XSEG/ref=sr_1_1?ie=UTF8&qid=1383451304&sr=8-1&keywords=Grape+solar+GS-P-280-fab1+280+watt (2"X39"X77")
- http://www.americanbombshelter.com
- http://www.americanbombshelter.com/flat-blast-

hatch.html
- http://www.americanbombshelter.com/60-CFM-ACDC-Safe-Cell-complete-system.html
- http://www.americanbombshelter.com/60-CFM-ACDC-Safe-Cell-complete-system.html
- http://www.americanbombshelter.com/120-CFM-ACDC-Safe-Cell-complete-system.html
- http://www.amsecusa.com/floor-safes/brute/
- http://www.backwoodssolar.com
- http://www.backyardaquaponics.com
- http://www.batteriesplus.com/product/33332-SLIGC110-6-volt-Battery/574-SLI/6067-Golf-Cart-Batteries/133277-E--Z--GO/TXT/TXT.aspx
- http://www.burpee.com
- http://www.bzproducts.net/id2.html
- http://www.campbound.com/Small-Camp-Trunk-Red.aspx?gclid=CKvkso-e2r4CFUOFOgodkBMACQ
- http://www.cheaperthandirt.com
- http://www.cheaperthandirt.com/product/MHR-316#
- http://www.directlyfromnature.com/
- http://diydrones.com/
- http://www.espring.com/
- https://www.facebook.com/groups/241463699375800/
- http://www.frontgate.com/stainless-steel-manual-trash-compactor/kitchen-entertaining/kitchen-storage-maintenance/543613?redirect=y
- http://www.homedepot.com/p/Flotec-85-Gal-Pre-Charged-Pressure-Tank-with-220-Gal-Equivalent-Rating-FP7130/100184364
- http://www.homedepot.com/p/LG-Electronics-2-3-cu-ft-Washer-and-Electric-Ventless-Dryer-in-White-WM3455HW/203218437?N=5yc1vZc3ot
- http://www.homedepot.com/p/Deer-X-7-ft-x-100-ft-Dalen-Products-Black-Polypropylene-Protective-Fencing-DX-7/202871745
- http://www.homedepot.com/p/Defiant-180-Degree-Outdoor-Motion-Activated-White-LED-Security-Floodlight-

MST18920LWDF/203303763?N=5yc1vZc7qf

- http://www.homedepot.com/p/TCG-Galvanized-Charcoal-or-Ash-Can-with-Lid-SR8012/203147413?N=Zbx82%2FNtk-Extended%2FNtt-garbage%252Bcan#.Upfo9uKOmSo
- http://www.homedepot.com/p/Air-King-Advantage-50-CFM-Ceiling-Exhaust-Fan-AS50/203258495?N=5yc1vZc4kqZ1z0umskZ1z0yi0z#specifications
- http://www.homedepot.com/p/US-Stove-900-sq-ft-Wood-Burning-Stove-1261/202245276?MERCH=REC-_-product-3-_-203630368-_-202245276-_-N#product_description
- http://www.homedepot.com/p/Eemax-Single-Point-2-4-kW-120-Volt-Electric-Tankless-Water-Heater-SP2412/203985266?N=5yc1vZc1tyZ2bcoqqZ1z0uhtu
- http://www.homedepot.com/p/Defiant-180-Degree-Outdoor-Black-Motion-Sensing-Security-Light-DF-5416-BK/203716689?N=5yc1vZc7qfZ1z0sk0s
- http://www.instructables.com/id/How-to-Weld---MIG-Welding/step2/How-the-Machine-Works/
- http://www.leeches.biz/
- http://www.lowes.com
- http://www.millerwelds.com/
- http://www.modernfoundations.com/
- http://www.monolithic.org
- http://www.nemoequipment.com/product/?p=Helio%20Pressure%20Shower
- http://www.newcenturydomebuilder.com/
- http://www.northmountainstructures.com/
- http://www.omick.net/composting_toilets/barrel_toilet.htm
- http://www.p3international.com/products/p4400.html
- https://www.pegasusautoracing.com/pro
- http://products.geappliances.com/ApplProducts/Dispatcher?REQUEST=SpecPage&Sku=JGB650DEFBB
- http://www.rakuten.com/prod/masterlock-security-bar-265dccsen/204290650.html

- http://www.ready.gov
- http://www.saniflo.com/homeowners/sfa-product-line/adaptable-grinders-and-lift-stations-for-small-spaces-and-commercial-buildings/
- http://www.thehomedepot.com
- http://www.walmart.com/c/kp/no-trespassing-signs
- http://www.weathershack.com/product/la-crosse-technology-ws-2815u-it.html
- http://www.wholesalesolar.com
- http://www.youtube.com
- http://www.youtube.com/watch?v=wzbPBx9KiuM

THE CONCEPT

THE idea is to create a secure, hidden, underground bunker in such a way to afford a couple, or small family (and pets), the ability to hide **comfortably** and indefinitely in the case of a doomsday scenario, SHTF or TEOTWAWKI (The End Of The World As We Know It). The way I have designed a bunker would afford more people the ability to join you in the bunker with only a few minor modifications. If you would like me to design a bunker for you that is larger or smaller, or different in any way, please contact me.

In the meantime, because of the way I designed the bunker, you can live in it permanently as if there were a doomsday scenario. The bunker would be your home. The bunker I designed would protect you from economic collapse, societal collapse, civil unrest, electromagnetic pulse, weather destruction, war, fire, terrorist attacks, nuclear incidents, fuel shortages, pandemics, geomagnetic reversal, and much more. The bunker would be able to sustain you for at least a year (depending on how much food and water you store), and possibly indefinitely, without your need to exit the bunker. The bunker itself will be completely underground. The roof of the bunker will be ten feet {three meters} below the surface.

You will be able to store food and fresh water. You will have the ability to bring in fresh air and water. You will have a fish tank and vegetable garden, and even some fruits.

My design for a bunker is to incorporate both a camouflaged main entrance and a separate camouflaged emergency exit. This way, if the main entrance collapses or otherwise becomes compromised, the bunker would not become your grave, you will have the second exit for emergencies. The entrance and exit will be about 180 feet {fifty-five meters} apart.

No one should know about the bunker. At the edge of your property, consider putting out a Gadsden Flag to let other preppers know you are willing to join a cooperative and help other preppers. As a prepper, you will have strength in numbers. The larger your cooperative, the better chance you have of survival.

If someone comes to you for help or to join you for a cooperative, I suggest you welcome them, cautiously. However, you should be prepared to defend yourselves and live alone if necessary. I suggest you try to find local, likeminded preppers to share resources and help. However, do not compromise your position for living and being safe. Facebook may be a good resource for you to find likeminded preppers. Just be very careful with whom you associate.

I also suggest you have drills to make sure you are able to completely close up the bunker and be secure in case of emergency, in a timely manner. This would include closing off the air and water pipes, enabling the booby-traps and securing the structure. I have several charts later in this book and on the website to assist you. You should also live completely off the grid as a practice for emergencies. Make a "bug-out" word you can use for drills or if the situation becomes real. You should also have practice drills to bug-out.

Before a SHTF scenario, you should live in the bunker to a large degree as if you were living in a doomsday situation. However, while living in the bunker before TSHTF, dispose of all waste and trash outside on the surface. Make a composting pit outside for all organic waste, burn what you can, and take other waste to the dump or recycling plant.

My design incorporates extensive security around the property and the security will get tighter and more extensive as one gets closer to the bunker. Some of the ideas and details for the security will be delineated herein, however most of the details will need to be setup in time, once you have the property and are in place.

Make sure to have some self entertainment in the bunker (cards, books, games, keyboard, videos, etc.).

Throughout this book, I will make suggestions as to how I am making my bunker. Feel free to use any part of what I have written here. I offer this information to you with all the research I have done, to make it easier for you.

When I give directions via the "clock", imagine you are standing in the center of the bunker facing the main door and the decontamination room at twelve O'clock. The halls will be behind you at six O'clock. Refer often to the sketches of the bunker at the end of this book.

Now let us begin...

OUTSIDE

FIND a large piece of property that is somewhat remote in order to give you significant privacy. Do not be so remote that there are no towns nearby. You want to be close enough where there are other stores and people, but not so close where you do not have your privacy. You will notice later, in the chapter on income, I suggest being close enough to be able to rent space on your property for a cell tower and maybe even a horse farm. If you are far from a town or two, you will not be able to have this passive income.

I suggest the property be at least five acres {20,230 square meters} in size to afford you the privacy and the ability to have the security you want. Before you purchase land, make sure to do PERC tests to confirm there is access to underground water for your well and the best location for your leach field. The addition of a stream on your property would also be advantageous.

For your own erudition, keep in mind the size of a football field, sideline to sideline, goalpost to goalpost is 57,600 square feet. If you remove the thirty feet on each end for the end-zone, you are left with 48,000 square feet. An acre is 43,560 square feet.

WWW.DOOMSDAYBUNKERBOOK.COM

DRIVEWAY

YOU WILL NEED SOME WAY to get from the public road to your compound. I suggest you have a dirt or gravel road leading from the public road. Do not make this road too wide as you do not want vehicles to be able to pass each other on your road. I suggest you make it about twelve feet wide. The reason for it being a dirt or gravel road is when a vehicle passes on your road, you will hear them coming. As we will discuss later, you will put a few IR sensors in the road to give you more warning of approaching vehicles.

Do what you can to camouflage the entrance from the public road onto your private driveway. You do not want it easily found.

Depending on your property, about twenty-five yards in, put a barricade or gate across the driveway so someone coming in will have a difficult time passing. Having trenches, boulders or heavy logs on either side of your driveway would serve two purposes.

1. A vehicle coming to your compound would have to stay on the gravel driveway. This would give you better control as to who accesses your compound.
2. Trenches would serve as drainage for your driveway and keep it in better condition.

As your driveway gets close to the compound, make a "choke point" or switch-back. This is a tight "S" curve that will make it more difficult for someone to approach without being detected. Place large boulders and logs on the edge of the road. The trees, boulders, logs and trenches, would make it impossible for an intruder to cut straight across your property directly to the compound.

These suggestions will have to be implemented after the construction is completed. The construction crews will require a straight line to the compound area.

COMPOUND

WHEN YOU LOOK AT THE overall drawing at the end of this book, you will notice there is a fence around most of the area. 135' {forty-one meters} X 200' {sixty-one meters}. This area is 27,000 square feet {2,508 square meters}. This is just one small part of the overall property. I call this area, the compound. Beyond the compound fencing is where you would put your traps. If you were to have a bee colony, you would place it outside the compound, a distance away. You do not want the bees visiting your compound.

Somewhat in the center of the property, on the surface, over what will be the front entrance of the bunker, have a surface structure of either a shed or a tire structure. We will discuss these structures later.

If someone were to raid the surface structure, the attacker can have the few cans of food and about one-hundred gallons {400 liter} of water you will keep inside. This will serve as a diversion. In the floor of the surface structure will be a hidden hatch that will be the entrance to your underground bunker. On the roof you will put solar panels for electricity. Also on the surface structure, put drains and downspouts to collect water.

On the four corners of the surface structure or in the trees, put up six to nine video cameras for surveillance. Depending on the location of the emergency exit, one or two of the video cameras may be covering the rear hatch.

Make a pond about fifty feet {fifteen meters} from the surface structure. Also put a fence in the front and the side of the surface structure, and a tire wall behind. More on these later in the book. Check the sketches at the end of this book to see how I am laying out my compound.

(Specifically for Jews) Put an *eruv* around the compound. The fences will be several segments of the *eruv*, the tire wall will be another. Check with your rabbi, as the laws of *eruv* are very complicated.

The solar energy system I delineate below would produce approximately 1KW per day. In order to live comfortably off the grid, you will need to at least double or even triple the system. More on that later.

You may need to take down some trees from the property or at least from the compound area. The reason for the removal of the trees is to afford a good view of the southern sky for solar panels and Dish Network (depending on where you live, this may be different). The wood will be available for your use as firewood. Set up a fire ring outside the surface structure.

Keep in mind that before TSHTF, you may want to spend much of your time in the surface structure. This may especially be so while you are still setting up your bunker and compound and if you want to meet with other people. Plan your surface structure accordingly.

SURFACE STRUCTURE

THERE are several options you have for a structure on the surface. Probably the easiest option would be to put a shed over your bunker entrance. You could find someone to build a shed for you, or purchase one already built, and have it delivered. Further in this book, I make suggestions as to how to secure the shed. For example, I suggest building up the inside wall with gravel and sand to protect against small weapons fire. The added weight will make it more secure in bad weather.

Another idea would be to build a structure made from used tires. There are many sites on the Internet that can show you how to make one. You will learn more from the Internet than I would be able to teach you in this book. My plan here is to give you ideas and guide you.

A third idea would be to use a steel shipping container. There are many options with a steel shipping container, however, I am not going into details. The reason is because they come in a variety of sizes and you have so many options for configuration. You will have to add doors, windows, seal the double-door at the one end, insulate the structure, cut a hole in the floor for the hatch, and more. I also do not like the roof of a steel shipping container as it would be difficult to collect water and put up the solar panels. Do research on the Internet as to what is best for you.

In any case, you would need a concrete pad for support. When you pour the concrete, do not forget to make accommodations for the hatch.

	SHED	TIRES
PROS	• Ready made • Easy to add solar panels • Easy to add gutters and downspouts • Already has a door, window, roof and floor	• Flexible size • Well insulated thick walls • Inexpensive
CONS	• Expensive • Not very flexible • Usually not insulated	• Takes time to make • Physically difficult to make • You have to make a roof • You have to make a floor

DIRT

AS WE WILL DISCUSS FURTHER, you will be excavating quite a bit of dirt for the bunker. The question is what to do with all that dirt. Some thoughts I have are: You can use it to make a wall for protection; help with your tire wall; build up the land of your compound to make it flatter and smoother; and much more. Keep the dirt on your property in case you need it, or you can sell some.

The following chart will give you some ideas as to what I recommend for both the shed and the tire structure.

SHED	If you use a shed, because of the weight inside the shed, you will need a decent foundation support. Raise the shed about eight inches onto cinder blocks (or concrete) that will be on a foundation slab, so you can hide the water pipes and for additional storage; extra gasoline, garden tools, supplies for your animals, and extra PVC, (*succah* for Jews). Attach to the studs inside the shed, 3/4" plywood. Fill the space behind the plywood with sand and stones. I suggest stones that are 1/2" - 3/4". The sand and stones will protect you from most gunfire and will also insulate the shed from cold. 160 CF of sand for a fourteen foot by twenty-four foot {4.3 X 7.3 meters} shed should cost about $150 (not including the plywood). Pour the sand and stones for the first six feet {1.8 meters} and if needed, use regular insulation above that. On the inside of the 3/4" plywood, attach sheet metal to add more protection from gun fire. Look into bullet proofing the windows of the shed. At the very least, put plexi-glass on the outside of the windows of the shed for cold weather and it will help to a small degree with gunfire.
TIRE STRUCTURE	The tire structure will need some sort of floor, but will not need the same type of foundation the shed would require as it will not be as heavy due to the lack of sand in the walls. Get a good solid door. I suggest a few windows, but make sure they are solid and preferably bullet proof. You will want a strong and solid roof to support the solar power system, collect water and protect against inclement weather.

BOTH	I suggest a structure that is at least fourteen feet by twenty-four feet {4.3 X 7.3 meters}. This size will give you enough space to do what is needed. For example, the roof will have solar panels, water acclimation system, surveillance cameras, antenna and cable dish. Inside the structure will be a few pieces of furniture for distraction, some water barrels, some basic supplies, the hatch and more. Put the generator outside the surface structure. The generator would only be used for emergencies.

Outside the surface structure, make a fire ring and have a Porta-Potty. You may even have a portable shower on the surface.

I also suggest you have the surface structure set up in such a way that you can actually live there. For example, a basic kitchen, bed, furniture and even the Porta-Potty and shower mentioned above. There are several reasons for this. One reason is to give the impression you actually live on the surface. When you meet with someone, for example for your goats, milk, eggs, or other reason, the visitor will not have an inkling you live below the surface in an underground bunker.

Another reason to have the surface structure set up for living is because you may actually want to spend time on the surface and this would make it more enjoyable and pleasant for you.

STRUCTURE

$\rm HIRE$ someone to build the structure of the bunker. The entire structure (including floors, walls and ceiling) will be four inches {ten centimeters} poured concrete. In order to make the structure sound, you will make it round with a monolithic dome. It is the round shape of the structure and the dome of the roof that gives the structure its strength to support the weight of the ten feet {three meters} of dirt above. This is the strongest way to build a structure. If you are in the continental United States of America, I know a reliable company who can build it for you. Here is their contact information. I ask that you please mention my name as they are building my bunker.

> David W. Smith
> 7941 Kaiyute Rd,
> Orange, Tx 77632
> 409-201-3644
> http://www.newcenturydomebuilder.com/

I would like to clarify something. Having an underground structure only four inches {ten centimeters} thick may seem a bit shabby and that it will not be strong enough to support itself and the tonnage of dirt above. However, due to the shape of the bunker being round and the roof being a monolithic dome, it will be plenty strong. Most contractors do not have experience building concrete structures nor monolithic domes. I have spoken with many contractors and structural engineers in doing research for this book and have found many will say they know what they are doing. However, once I started asking questions, I found they are woefully ignorant. This is why I recommend the company mentioned above. Please be careful.

Just to give you an idea, to build the bunker to my specifications, should cost approximately based on the chart below (do not hold me to these numbers as they may change). This is for the United States:

Excavation	$20,000-$30,000
Construction	Shell $60-$90 per SF
	Finished $110-$160 per SF

The inside of the bunker will have a diameter of thirty feet {9.15 meters}. There will also be a decontamination room, three halls, two sets of stairs, an entrance and an emergency exit. See the architectural drawings at the end of this book for more details. All measurements herein are for the internal spaces and do not include the thickness of the walls. All walls, slabs and the dome will be four inches {10.2 centimeters} thick.

LEVEL	S.F.	S.M.
Basement	707	65.7
Main level	707	65.7
Bedroom	707	65.7
Decontamination room	140	13
Halls (3) (175 SF @)	525	49
Entrance ramp	325	30.2
Emergency exit ramp	267	25
Surface structure	336	31.2
TOTAL SF	3,714	345.5

Unfortunately, due to the curve around the perimeter of the inside of the bunker, you lose quite a bit of space around the edge. This is why I designed the bunker to be so large. The bedroom level will have a monolithic dome that will start two feet {sixty-one centimeters} up from the floor. Due to the curve of the dome, on the top floor, you lose about three feet {91.5 centimeters} around the perimeter. The bedroom level will be a total of fourteen feet {4.3 meters} tall at its apex. Because the concrete is so thick and so far underground, you do not need to insulate. The curve of the monolithic dome needs to be at the least 0.33:(the diameter of the bunker). This means, if the diameter of your bunker is thirty-one feet {9.5 meters}, including the walls, the dome needs to be at least 10.23' {3.2 meters} tall. My design calls for the bedroom level being fourteen feet {4.3 meters}, which includes twelve feet {2.7 meters} for the dome and two feet {45.7 centimeters} for the wall before the dome starts.

The structure itself will have three levels. The main level will be eight feet {2.5 meters} tall and will house the kitchen, office, command center, shower, living room and dining room. The entrance will be to this level. The lower level will also be eight feet {2.5 meters} tall and will be used for storage. The upstairs will be both bedroom and additional storage. However, if you want to have more than just one couple in your bunker (children, family), make the entire upstairs level into bedrooms and all the storage would be in the basement.

Outside height will be about thirty-one feet {9.5 meters} plus the foundation. This does not include the bathroom area, halls and stairs that would extend out the back of the bunker. The hall areas will be twenty-five feet {7.6 meters} by seven feet {2.2 meters}. As mentioned, all slabs will be four inch {10.2 centimeters} poured concrete.

From the main level, at the six O'clock position, there will be an exterior door that leads to the main hall which will have the bathroom, trash tube, stairs, composting pit and emergency exit. Put a curtain to close off the bathroom for some privacy. By the bathroom will be a trash tube that will be four feet by four feet {1.2X1.2 meters} and twelve feet {3.7 meters} long with a downward angle.

Waterproof the outside of the bunker. Have drainage pipes built into the foundation for the sump pump. Have the sump pump drain in such a way to be able to use the water. The sump pump will be in storage area 46, so it will be close to the water storage tanks. It is quite probable you will not need to use the sump pump at all. Built into the same foundation will be a radon amelioration system.

The roof of the bunker will be ten feet {three meters} below the surface to protect from chemical, biological and radiation poisoning. As a side effect of being below the surface, you will not have to concern yourself with sound, weather, heat or cold, rot, warp or rust. You will also not have to worry about bugs or water. Depending on where you are going to be building your bunker, the ambient inside temperature should be a consistent fifty-five degrees Fahrenheit {12.8 degrees Celsius}; the heating will be minimal while the cooling needs will be non-existent. A concrete structure that is completely covered with dirt, will be completely insulated.

Dirt weighs seventy-eight pounds {35.4 kilogram} per CF. There will be approximately 9,000 CF of dirt above the bunker. This means there will be approximately 702,000 pounds (351 tons) of dirt above the bunker. Excavate down about forty-five feet for a total of about 58,000 CF of dirt. This would include space for the halls, decontamination room and ramps. As mentioned above, a monolithic dome roof for the bunker would make it completely stable from the pressure of all that dirt.

The toilet will be behind a curtain near the emergency exit, storage area 64. The toilet will dump into an external septic system. More details further on. The dog "spot" (where it will do its business inside the bunker) will be storage area 61 just before entering into the main level hall.

Raise the bed a few inches with bricks to make storage underneath. Put a shelf above the doors, and fridge. Make shelves above the toilet for toiletries.

Raise up the shower to be able to collect gray water to be used in the toilet. To make the shower, purchase a shower kit and a shower curtain. Put a tarp under the shower and sink.

On the end of some of the shelves, above the bed, in some storage areas, and the stairwells, feel free to put up photos and other personal mementoes.

During construction, bring in all major appliances and large objects: IBC's, stove, fridge, freezer, washer/dryer, pellet stove, wood stove, etc.

Hang nylon rope from the ceiling of the main level for drying laundry. You may or may not have a clothes dryer in the bunker. Either way, during a SHTF scenario, you will not want to use the dryer in order to save energy.

Another suggestion I have is to do something with the floor. I suggest putting down tile. You do not want to walk barefoot on concrete, so you want to have something on which to walk. If you are planning to live there full time, as do I, put down tile and get some throw rugs.

DOOR SCHEDULE

1	Surface structure door	External steal door
2	Front hatch	Blast hatch
3	Ramp into decontamination room	External steal door

4	Decontamination room into bunker	External steal door
5	Bunker into main hall	External steal door
6	Hall into bedroom	External steal door
7	Hall into storage room	External steal door
8	Hall into emergency exit	External steal door
9	Emergency exit hatch	Blast hatch
10	Composting pit	Hatch door
11	Trash tube	Hatch door

FRONT ENTRANCE

THE front hatch will be a thirty-two inch by thirty-eight inch {eighty-one centimeters by ninety-one centimeters} flat blast hatch built into the floor of the surface structure.

This is what I recommend for the blast hatch. http://www.americanbombshelter.com/flat-blast-hatch.html. However, any of their hatches are great.

Weld to the inside of the hatch brackets to support a bar to prevent someone from opening the hatch. Get an electromagnetic locking system for more security.

Inside the opening of the hatch will be a foam pad that will be used for insulation from cold, sound, and will add an extra layer of protection from chemical penetration. Attached to the inside of the door of the decontamination room (door 3) will be another foam pad.

Booby-trap the entrance. Details further on.

The front ramp will be seven feet {2.2 meters} tall in order to have room for the pipes. There will be two (2), four inch {ten centimeters} PVC pipes. One pipe will be for water and one for wires. The pipes and wires will be discussed further. The wires do not have to be inside of a pipe the entire length of the ramp. The ramp would be about one-hundred feet {thirty meters} long, 3.5' {one meter} wide. The exact length will be determined by your specific location.

At the bottom of the ramp will be an exterior door that will open into the decontamination room. The decontamination room will be discussed in the next chapter.

DECONTAMINATION ROOM

AS part of the main entrance of the bunker, make a decontamination room. The decontamination room will serve several purposes. It will act as a mud room; coat room; storage for outdoor supplies; some water tanks; sump pump; gas mask and body suit storage. The room will also be a blockage for radiation and chemical poisoning. Radiation does not go around corners so the decontamination room will be at a ninety degree turn from the bunker.

The size of the decontamination room will be ten feet {three meters} wide by thirteen feet {four meters} long by thirteen feet {four meters} tall. The floor of the decontamination room will be even with that of the bunker. The reason for the height of the decontamination room is to accommodate the two IBC water tanks that will be discussed later on in the water chapter.

Put a barricade on the inside of the door (door 3) to prevent ingress from intruders. Against the inside of the door will be another foam pad for insulation. Use bungee cords to hold it in place against the door.

The door leading into the bunker from the decontamination room (door 4) will also be an exterior steel door that will be well insulated and open into the bunker. Put a barricade on the inside of the door to prevent ingress from intruders. Against the inside of the door will be another foam pad for insulation. Use bungee cords to hold it in place against the door. Both doors of the decontamination room may not be open at the same time. One of the doors must be closed at all times to prevent contamination from the outside.

On the bottom of both of the doors put door sweeps for added insulation.

Storage area 46 will have the sump pump and on the top shelf will be a fifty-five gallon {208 liter} barrel to hold additional water.

Storage area 44 will be for the solar system controls, batteries, inverter, circuit breakers etc. Make this area into a large faraday cage. Make an aluminum box that is covered on the interior with cardboard. Read further for instructions on how to make a faraday cage to protect the electrical system from electromagnetic pulses.

LIVING

DAY-to-day living in a bunker will be challenging. I hope this book will help you plan, and give you some tips and pointers to make your life easier.

To this end, you will probably want to get a clothes washer and dryer. I have spent considerable time researching this subject. This is the unit I recommend:
http://www.homedepot.com/p/LG-Electronics-2-3-cu-ft-Washer-and-Electric-Ventless-Dryer-in-White-WM3455HW/203218437?N=5yc1vZc3ot.

The reasons I like this unit are:
1. It does not require venting, and
2. It combines both a washer and dryer in one unit.

Here is a small manual washing machine for when you have to conserve energy:
http://www.amazon.com/gp/product/B005FD7Z82/ref=as_li _qf_sp_asin_il_tl?ie=UTF8&camp=1789&creative=9325&c reativeASIN=B005FD7Z82&linkCode=as2&tag=preppersw or05-20&linkId=HAH5KI62OIV4PZHG

You may want to get a dish washing machine. Personally, I am not going to get one as it will use too much water and electricity, never-the-less, it is something you may want to consider.

Much of your time may be spent on the surface taking care of the animals and enjoying the fresh outside air. Make sure you have some supplies in or under the surface structure to accommodate any needs. This would include some gardening tools, drinking water, some high energy snacks (GORP) and more.

In the bunker design, you will notice each level is open architecture. There are several reasons for this. Walls take up to four to five inches and you do not have much space to spare. It is also easier to heat this type of space.

Another item you may want to consider is a dehumidifier. Most likely this will not be necessary. However, it would be good to have one on hand.

Keep in mind you may be living here long term, either because you want to or because of a doomsday scenario. You will want some creature comforts with you in the bunker.

You may want to get some motion detection lights for the halls and stairwells. Maybe some nightlights. This will make it easier when walking around. Keep in mind there are no windows to let in outside light; the bunker will be pitch black without your own lights.

You may also want to put ceiling fans on both the bedroom levels and the main level to help with air movement.

ENTERTAINMENT

LIVING IN AN UNDERGROUND BUNKER for an extended period, could lead to psychological and emotional problems. You will need ways to combat these forms of stress that can tear you and your family apart. You want to live a productive life and part of that is making a living. We will talk about that aspect in the chapter on income. In this section, I want to talk with you about other forms of dealing with the loss of normal family and community interactions. This is a subject rarely, if ever, mentioned in other bunker books.

Boredom is going to be a major factor living in a bunker, especially long term with no one else around.

I will make a few suggestions to help you. In the upstairs hall, storage area 36, set up an area for exercising. I am not concerned with what you purchase, just make sure you and your entire family gets regular exercise.

Make sure to have plenty of books and games that do not use electricity or batteries.

Do not forget your spiritual health. Have plenty of religious books and paraphernalia. This is equally as important, if not more so, than your physical and mental health.

Personally, I am going to have a pool table that will double as the dining room table. Have games that are age appropriate for your children as they grow.

REAR EXIT

THE emergency exit (door 11) will be a flat blast hatch thirty-two inches by thirty-two inches {eighty-two centimeters by eighty-two centimeters} that will open out. Weld to the hatch sheet metal brackets to support a bar to prevent someone from opening the hatch and invading. Get an electromagnetic locking system for more security. Inside the opening of the hatch will be a foam pad that will be used for insulation from weather and sound, and will add an extra layer of protection from chemical penetration. (Try to make the rear hatch similar to the front hatch.) Attached to the inside of the door (door 8) of the entrance of the bunker will be another foam pad for insulation and chemical protection. Put a barricade against door 8. As there is no structure over the emergency exit hatch, you want to camouflage and insulate this very well against weather and chemical or biological contamination.

The back ramp will be six feet {1.9 centimeters} tall, about ninety feet {27.5 meters} long and three feet {0.9 meters} wide. The exact length will be determined by your specific location.

The emergency exit will be outside the compound so if your compound becomes compromised, you still have an escape. Electrify the emergency hatch. Booby-trap the emergency exit. For the booby-trap, have a car battery hooked up to a plate on the ramp so when someone steps on it, they will get a shock. Put a kill-switch hidden in the wall. Put a taut fishing wire across the ramp about six inches {fifteen centimeters} from the floor so an intruder will trip. Put bubble wrap on the floor so if someone steps on it, you will hear them.

Make sure to camouflage the emergency exit very well as it will be outside of the compound and there will be no structure above it, cover it with sand and/or dirt, leaves, branches, etc. I am more concerned with the security of the emergency exit than with the main entrance, as the emergency exit will not be as well hidden. Have the hatch buried under a foot or two {thirty to sixty centimeters} of dirt.

The door leading from the bunker to the ramp (door 8) will be an exterior steel door that will be well insulated and will open into the bunker. Put a barricade on the inside of the door to prevent ingress from intruders. As in the front, put a foam pad on the inside of the bunker door for added insulation. Use bungee cords to keep it in place against the door. This door will only be used in case of emergency.

Have a complete bug-out kit per person, plus any pets. Store them in storage area 69. Have a few additional bug-out kits hidden in the woods with more supplies. The hidden bug-out kits should contain mostly food, some first aid and maybe some barter items. Consider using five gallon {nineteen liter} buckets. Put supplies inside of sealed plastic bags; put the bags inside the buckets and seal them, then burry them in the ground, at least two feet {sixty centimeters} deep.

Once the emergency exit is closed, it should only need to be checked on occasion. Door 8 should not be opened.

CONSTRUCTION NOTES

THIS chapter will give notes for the construction of the bunker. Most of this chapter is mentioned elsewhere in this book, but collated here to make it easier and give you more details. Some of this section is gleaned from www.americanbombshelter.com, and engineers. I also highly recommend their blast hatches and their air filtration system. No, I do not get a kickback from them, and you need not mention me.

Before you get started, you will need to have an engineer look over your plans. In most states you will need engineering stamps before you can proceed.

During the construction of the bunker, you will probably want to be on site as much as possible. I plan to be on site the entire time the crews will be doing the excavation and construction. To that end, since I eventually plan to purchase an RV in order to be able to bug-out if necessary, I will purchase an RV and live in it on site until I am able to move into the bunker. You may want to do the same.

During construction, bring in all appliances, furniture, wood stove, pellet stove, IBC's, and anything else that will not easily fit in through the hatch.

- A bunker needs to have two exit points in case one of them becomes compromised.
- A bunker needs to be deep enough to be protected from radiation and chemical penetration - about ten feet.
- All doors should be steel, exterior, insulated doors.
- All doors must be able to be locked securely from the inside.
- Hatches must open **out**.
- **AN AIRLOCK**. The easiest way to incorporate an airlock in your bunker, is to put your NBC filter as far away from the door as possible, flow the air through your shelter toward your door, then out a blast valve adjacent to - or above - the door and out into a stairway or hallway that has a gas-tight door on the other end. You will need another overpressure valve adjacent to that gas-tight door. If you set it up this way, all the air in that hallway or stairway will be flowing one way - out of your shelter. We will be adapting this concept for use in your bunker.
- **NO DEAD SPACES IN THE AIRFLOW**. The air comes in through the intake pipe, goes through the air filter, and is introduced into the shelter out the top port of the air filter. From here, it finds its way to the overpressure valve on the outflow blast valve. Where you place the filter and the outflow blast valve determines exactly where the air "finds its way." They should be at opposite ends of your bunker. Storage rooms need less airflow than living spaces.
- **COMMAND CENTER**. There should be one place in the bunker where your detection, observation, and communication equipment is located - the command center. One spot where one person can be stationed to deal with anything going on inside and outside the

bunker. In our case, I suggest this be part of the office area.

- **MECHANICAL ROOM**. This is optional. Most shelters have a mechanical room or area where the air filter and electrical system is located. One advantage of this design is your critical life support equipment can be in one place. I suggest this be part of the decontamination room, however, the air filter would not be here as it would not be an efficacious location in our design.
- **KITCHEN AND BATHROOM.** Every shelter should have at least one of each. Things to look out for: Vents and drains that may leak unfiltered air in, vents and drains that are not protected from nearby detonations with a blast valve, and carbon monoxide being generated by cook stoves.
- **PIPES**. For the exact location of the holes and pipes, please see the architectural drawings.

BLAST PROTECTION

MANY UNDERGROUND SHELTERS ARE BUILT to be able to resist blast pressures, but their portals to the outside (entrance and exit) need protection as well. It makes no sense to have a shelter that will withstand high pressure blast waves and not install blast doors and blast valves. A detonation imparts several pressure waves – incident (direct), reflective, and a combined incident and reflective wave called the Mach Stem. These high pressure waves blow the atmosphere out from the point of detonation creating a momentary vacuum - a dramatic drop in air pressure. This vacuum is dangerous to equipment and occupants of a shelter.

BLAST VALVES are devices installed over the ventilation pipes inside your shelter. They are normally open to low pressure air moving in both directions. When a high pressure wave comes over your shelter, the valve automatically shuts. When the vacuum that follows the pressure wave comes over your shelter, the blast valve will also close. Then, it will return to its neutral position - letting the NBC filter move low pressure air into and out of your shelter.

BLAST DOORS should have a pressure rating and a rebound load rating. To handle as much pressure as possible, all swinging blast doors should swing outward so the pressure load is taken in the seated position - transferred directly from the door leaf to the frame. If the door were to swing inward, the load would travel from the door leaf, through the latches and hinges, and then to the frame. It is more efficient to have the door leaf act as a bridge between the sides of the frame and take the load in the seated position.

The rebound load rating need not be greater than negative 14.5 PSI (one bar). This is the standard air pressure at sea level - when you remove the air, you can only go down to a vacuum (zero pressure). The latches and hinges need to be engineered to take this negative one bar load without failing.

AIR FILTRATION

ONCE YOU GO TO THE time and expense of constructing an effective blast shelter, air filtration must be considered. The only real choice for collective protection is a Nuclear, Biological, and Chemical (NBC) overpressure air filtration system. The NBC filter elements consist of a pre-filter to collect the large particles, a HEPA filter for the fine particles, and a carbon absorber for the gases and vapors. It is connected to the blast valve that is mounted over the air intake ventilation pipe.

The HEPA filter is tasked with removing the particulates and aerosols from the airstream. There are many types of "HEPA" filters available. Not all of them are suitable for protection against radioactive fallout. The best filters are **individually** scan tested. They are individually challenged with an inert aerosol that duplicates the properties of what you are trying to protect from – such as dioctyl pthalate (DOP). If you have a HEPA filter without a serial number, chances are good it has **not** been individually tested.

The carbon absorber is placed after the HEPA filter. Its purpose is to absorb the toxic gases present in the airstream. The residency time of the air in the granular carbon bed must be engineered so the carbon has enough time to absorb the toxic vapors present in the air. Room air filters with shallow carbon beds for "odor control" are not suitable for this type of filtration.

An effective NBC filter will have a way to operate the filter when power is interrupted. Most have a manual (hand operated) backup system. The Safe Cell (the one I am recommending) also features a battery backup system that will keep the filter in operation for up to twenty-four hours. (Have a second battery charged to double that time.) This system has been evaluated by the US State Department and found to be a Class IV Munitions because of its level of air filtration. Another credible set of standards are the ones met by Israeli air filtration equipment.

Once you have proper filtration, what you do with that filtered air is critical. To ensure all the air in your shelter is flowing outward - and not letting toxins migrate inside, you need to have positive pressure in relation to the outside. This is known as overpressure. The US Army Corp of Engineers considers 0.3 inches of water gauge a Class 1 Toxic Free Area. This is relatively low pressure – 0.0108 PSI, but it is enough to ensure toxins do not migrate into your shelter through any cracks.

VENTILATION

VENTILATION IS HOW YOU MOVE air from the outside, flow through, and then back out of your shelter. You can do this with filtered or fresh air. Proper ventilation replenishes the oxygen supply and removes the carbon dioxide and moisture occupants exhale. Ideally, you should bring the air into your shelter in one corner and expel it in the opposite corner. This is not always possible (especially with a **round** bunker), but you should position the intake and outflow ventilation pipes as far apart as possible to avoid short circuiting the airflow and creating dead spots that do not get sufficient air exchanges.

If you have multiple rooms in your shelter, the air should be routed through as many of them as possible. The room the NBC air filter is located should have an overpressure valve between it and the rest of the shelter in case you lose your grid or solar power, then exhaust the battery, and are down to hand powered filtration and ventilation. When powering your filter by hand, you want to have as small a space as possible to protect. The overpressure valve helps the filter to create and maintain overpressure by restricting and regulating the outflow of air - it opens to release air only when the pressure in the room gets up to a certain pressure. It also acts as a check valve, not allowing air to flow back into the protected space.

Once the air leaves that room, it should flow throughout the shelter until it is expelled through the outflow system - which should consist of an overpressure valve, a blast valve, and an outflow ventilation pipe where the air is expelled outside the shelter. If there are multiple rooms, the vents between the rooms the air moves through should be on opposite corners and at different heights in order to get the best ventilation.

SURFACE STRUCTURE

THERE WILL BE A CONCRETE foundation under the surface structure to support its weight. If the surface structure is a shed, then raise it up about a foot {thirty centimeters} to be able to hide the water and electrical pipes and the blast hatch. Since the surface structure will be raised up, take advantage of the space and use it for storage. If using a tire structure, you will not be able to raise it, however, you could put in a raised wood floor.

FRONT RAMP

THE FRONT RAMP WILL BE made of concrete and be seven feet {2.1 meters} tall. The ramp will be about one-hundred feet {30.5 meters} long (depending on your property) and three and a half feet wide {one meter}, interior measurements. The ramp will open from a hole in the surface structure. This will be a flat blast hatch that opens **out** into the surface structure. Use a flat blast hatch that is thirty-two inches by thirty-eight inches {eighty-one centimeters by ninety-seven centimeters}. Surround the entrance of the bunker that is located under the shed with concrete, so it is well hidden.

Running along the ceiling of the ramp will be a water pipe. This pipe will be four inches {ten centimeters} PVC. The electrical cables will also be running along the ceiling, but the pipe for the wires does not need to be the entire length. The door leading to the decontamination room will be a steel exterior door that opens **into** the decontamination room.

EXIT RAMP

THE EMERGENCY EXIT RAMP WILL be made of concrete and be six feet {1.8 meters} tall. The ramp will be about ninety feet {27.5 meters} long (depending on your property) and three feet {0.9 meters} wide, interior measurements. The exit of the ramp will be a solid hatch that opens **out** from the ramp. Use a flat blast hatch that is 32"X32" {81 centimeters by 81 centimeters}.

The door leading from the exit ramp to the hall of the bunker, will be a steel exterior door that opens **into** the hall.

DECONTAMINATION ROOM

THE FLOOR OF THE DECONTAMINATION room will be even with the bunker. However, the decontamination room will be thirteen feet {four meters} tall. In the decontamination room will be some water storage, the electrical components of the solar system, outdoor supplies and more. The water pipe will come through here and empty into two IBC's and then continue into the bunker to two more IBC's. There also needs to be a hole in the wall to bring cables from the ramp into the decontamination room and then into the bunker. Make sure to seal all the holes.

HALLS

THERE WILL BE A HALL at the back of each bunker level at six O'clock. To access each hall, there will be a steel exterior door that opens **into** the bunker from each hall. Each hall will be seven feet by twenty five feet {2.1 meters by 7.6 meters} interior measurements.

The bedroom level hall (top floor) will have the incoming water from the well. At this juncture, there will be a shut-off valve in-line. The water pipe will then continue down through the floor to the main level. The water will then continue into the bunker itself and there will be an additional shut-off valve inside. The pipe will then run along the ceiling to the kitchen area.

The main level hall (middle floor) will have the toilet that dumps into the exterior septic system. Also in the main level hall will be a trash tube and a composting pit. Both of these will be off the back wall of the hall. The emergency exit ramp will also be on this level.

The basement level hall (bottom floor) will not have anything special on it. However, store the freezer down here under the stairs, where there can be additional storage, as well.

There will be stairs going from the storage level up through the main and bedroom levels. The stairs will go up from the side closer to the bunker.

FOUNDATION

THE ENGINEERS I SPOKE WITH, suggest the foundation slab should be four inches thick of poured concrete. The foundation ring beam (below the four inch foundation slab) should be the circumference of the bunker and be twelve inches wide by twelve inches deep. For the reinforcement of the foundation ring beam 3 #4 rebar 60 grade.

The concerns I have with the foundation are as follows:

- Inside the ring beam, place two-inch gravel to allow for the sump pump and radon pipes
- Have drainage pipes around the circumference (inside the ring beam) for drainage into the sump pump
- Have perforated pipes laid out for passive radon amelioration
- Both sets of pipes will be inside the foundation ring amongst the two inch gravel

BASEMENT

AT THE TWELVE O'CLOCK POSITION in the basement, build a safe into the floor. On all six sides of the inside of the safe, put cardboard to make it into a faraday cage. There are no other specific construction concerns I have for the basement. This is what I recommend for a safe. http://www.amsecusa.com/floor-safes/brute/

MAIN LEVEL

INSTALL A GROUNDING ROD OUTSIDE the bunker. The front and back doors will open **into** the bunker to be able to barricade the doors. Have all appropriate holes in the wall and floor formed during the construction; for air, water, PVC pipes and cables.

In the floor of the main level at both twelve O'clock and six O'clock make a ten inch by ten inch {25.4 centimeter} hole to allow some air movement to the basement.

BEDROOM

IN THE FLOOR OF THE bedroom, at both twelve O'clock and six O'clock make a ten inch by ten inch {25.4 centimeter} hole to accommodate an air fan that will be used for internal air movement between the main level and the bedroom level. The monolithic dome will start two feet {sixty-one centimeters} above the floor and the dome itself will be twelve feet {3.7 meters}. This brings the total internal height of the bedroom level to fourteen feet {4.3 meters} at its apex.

www.monolithic.org for information on the air form for the dome.

AIR SYSTEM

I am going to give you two possible scenarios for the air filtration system. Depending on how much effort and money you are willing to put into your air system, will determine which of these two systems you will utilize. The NBC is the better system and in my opinion, well worth the money.

NBC AIR SYSTEM

NBC STANDS FOR NUCLEAR, BIOLOGICAL, and Chemical. An NBC filter protects against all three forms of air contamination. This type of filter creates a positive overpressure in the bunker. The Safe Cell air filtration system (made by American Bomb Shelter) works by drawing outside air through its filter banks and introducing it into the bunker creating a slight overpressure. This overpressure prevents unfiltered air or toxins from migrating into the bunker through any openings or cracks. The overpressure relief valve is the variable factor which governs airflow and overpressure in an airtight shelter. An airflow of 5-CFM (cubic feet per minute) per person is recommended.

An airtight shelter must have an exhaust vent with an overpressure valve installed on an opposite wall from the filtration unit output to ensure the sufficient per occupant ventilation rate is taking place as well as proper overpressure.

http://www.americanbombshelter.com/60-CFM-ACDC-Safe-Cell-complete-system.html

http://www.americanbombshelter.com/120-CFM-ACDC-Safe-Cell-complete-system.html

Either of these systems is what I recommend. The reason for this recommendation is it affords a very high quality for what is needed for the air filtration. This system also has dual back-ups in case of electricity failure.

There will be two 4" PVC pipes for incoming air. The following is detailed instructions on how to make this work.

The surface mounts of the pipes must be camouflaged very well. Have screens to prevent debris from entering the pipes and make a mound of stones in such a way to prevent blockage of the pipes from debris, water and snow. Maybe put a deer blind over the pipes.

Both pipes will start above the surface from a 180 degree down-turned 4" PVC pipe. These two pipes will run along the inside of the bunker wall at both twelve O'clock and six O'clock. At the very point where these two pipes enter the bunker in the bedroom, have a shut-off valve.

The NBC filter, overpressure relief valve and its back-up battery will continue down to the main level. These will be at the six O'clock position with the bottom about four feet {1.2 meters} off the floor to accommodate some storage or the "dog spot" underneath.

The overpressure relief valve will be at the twelve O'clock position in the bedroom and go back out to the surface. There will be a 4" hole in the floor of the bedroom below the overpressure relief valve to accommodate air movement.

Below both these pipes, in the floor of the main level, will be 4" holes to have some air movement in the basement.

BASIC AIR SYSTEM

THERE WILL BE TWO 4" PVC pipes for incoming air. The following is detailed instructions on how to make this work.

The surface mounts of the pipes must be camouflaged very well. Have screens to prevent debris from entering the pipes and make a mound of stones in such a way to prevent blockage of the pipes from debris, water and snow. Maybe put a deer blind over the pipes.

Both pipes will start above the surface from a 180 degree down-turned 4" PVC pipe. These two pipes will run along the inside of the bunker wall at both twelve O'clock and six O'clock. At the very point where these two pipes enter the bunker in the bedroom, have a shut-off valve. These pipes will continue into the basement.

Both pipes will have a "T" connection at the ceiling of all three levels. All three levels will have screens and two or three watt fans to bring air into the bunker. On each level, immediately prior to the fans will be shut-off valves and air filters. Have a ball FPT PVC pipe to close off the pipes for additional protection from outside air contamination. Also put a clean-out by the air filters in the front and back.

NOTES

HAVING THE GARDEN AND ALL the other plants on the main level in the bunker will give you plenty of O_2 and will help clean the air in the bunker. With this in mind, if there is an emergency outside and you have to close off the air supply, you need not be concerned. You should have no problems with the air system. However, due to the efficacy and quality of the NBC filter system, you should have no problems leaving it on even in a SHTF scenario.

DIY air filter http://4volt.com/Blog/archive/2009/06/09/diy-3-stage-air-filter.aspx

Both the wood pellet stove and the wood stove will have metal pipes that go straight up and through the bedroom level and then continue to the surface. The purpose for the pipes going through the bedroom level is for heat in the bedroom. Camouflage the ends at the surface well. Have a blast valve on both of these pipes in case there is a detonation, the blast valve will automatically shut off these pipes.

Just prior to the vent going through the ceiling of the main level of the bunker, have a junction to put in a fan in order to be able to exhaust the bunker in case of internal emergencies.

Purchase and use a few CO detectors.

INTERNAL AIR FLOW

IN THE FLOOR OF THE bedroom, near the wall at both twelve O'clock and six O'clock will be holes for venting air between the main level and the bedroom level. These vents will have fifty CFM fans in them that will be available to be used as needed. Most of the time, the fans will not be used. However, when TSHTF, they will be used continuously to move air **from** the main level in the front (where the garden is), **to** the upstairs, and then back down again at the back of the bunker. Do not permanently mount these fans, as this will allow you to turn the fans around as needed to direct the air movement.

In the floor of the main level at both twelve O'clock and six O'clock make a ten inch by ten inch {25.4 centimeter} hole to allow some air movement to the basement.

Cut a 4" hole in the wall from each level to the halls of each level to get some air movement into the halls.

WATER

WWW.READY.GOV suggests we have one gallon of water per person per day for fourteen days. Personally, I say you should triple the amount and plan for at least a month, because during the summer, you will become dehydrated and want to ration your water. If you can avoid it, do not ration your water. Always make sure you are drinking enough water; rather ration your washing water. Do not forget to stock water for your pets and any other animals for which you are responsible. Water is one thing you do not want to be without.

Water weighs 8.34 pounds per gallon. A fifty-five gallon {208 liter} water barrel is twenty-four inches {sixty-one centimeters} diameter, thirty-six inches {91.5 centimeters} tall. 22.5 pounds {10.2 kilos} tare weight.

After significant research, I recommend the eSpring UV water purifier. In my opinion, this is the best filter and the only one that incorporates a high quality UV purification system. This system will purify 1,320 gallons {5,000 liters} per filter change. If you need a distributor for the eSpring filter, please contact me, I will put you in touch with someone reliable.

DAILY WATER SUPPLY

DIG A WELL ON THE property that will supply water throughout the bunker. The well should be situated between ten to forty feet from the bunker. The well should be as deep as necessary to ensure a good water supply and refresh rate. The well will have a jet pump. This means the pump will be inside the bunker on the upstairs landing. The reason for the pump being inside is to have access to the pump for maintenance and repair. Additionally, have a way to bring water to the surface for use in your surface structure and for the animals. I cannot go into details here as there are too many variables to take into consideration. You will have to make a determination as to what will work best, once you have your property.

The well water will come in via the bedroom level hall and have a shut-off valve as soon as it enters. At the upstairs hall will be the pump and a water pressure tank. The water pressure tank is to facilitate having water pressure in your bunker. The pressurized water tank measures twenty-four inches {sixty-one centimeters} diameter, fifty-three inches {135 centimeters} tall and hold about eighty-five gallons {322 liters} (129 pounds {58.5 kilos} tare). Consider putting a shelf above the tank for storage. Have the tank upstairs in order to facilitate water flow. As the water leaves the tank, the water will go through a water filter (maybe the eSpring brand mentioned above). Have a spigot in the upstairs hall to allow access to water at the bedroom level.

The water will flow through a pipe that goes through the floor and into the bathroom area (not to the toilet). At this point, there will be another shut-off valve and then it will continue into the main part of the bunker. It will continue along the ceiling to the kitchen area. The water pipe will split into two hoses with a "Y" adapter that has levers to shut off the water. One of the hoses will supply a tank-less water heater and the other will be for cold water. Both the tank-less water heater and cold water pipes will feed hoses into the sink and shower.

EMERGENCY WATER STORAGE

ON THE SURFACE STRUCTURE, ATTACH rain gutters with gutter guards and flexible downspouts. Each flexible downspout will travel to the inside of the surface structure and each one will empty into a fifty-five gallon {208 liter} water barrel. The barrels will be raised up onto cinder blocks. There will be a screen at the top of each barrel to filter any additional debris the gutter guards did not catch. From the bottom of each barrel will be a hose with a shut-off valve that will go to a "Y" and another hose that will go into a four inch PVC pipe in the ramp of the bunker. There will be an additional screen at the outlet of each barrel to catch even more debris.

The water pipe will continue along the ceiling of the ramp into the bunker through the decontamination room. As it passes into the decontamination room, have a ball FPT PVC pipe to close off the pipe for additional protection from outside water contamination. This water will empty into a fifty-five gallon {208 liter} water barrel. The barrel will be kept on the top shelf in the decontamination room. Unless additional water is needed, this valve will be kept closed. From the barrel, the water will continue through another series of screens and filters and empty into the upper IBC. From here the water will flow into the lower of the two IBC's.

There will also be incoming water from the pond. At the pond, make a culvert with stones (permeable dam) and screens to filter out any debris. From the pond, there will be a four inch PVC pipe that will lead to the ramp and connect with a "T" to the main water pipe. Just prior to the "T", have a ball FPT PVC shut-off valve and clean-out.

As noted elsewhere, the decontamination room will be thirteen feet {400 centimeters} tall. Raise up the IBC's (Intermediate Bulk Container) as high as possible.

From the lower IBC, a PVC pipe will go up and through the wall into the bunker. The water will then continue into the third IBC. You may need a water pump to get the water from IBC 2 to IBC 3. From this third IBC, water will feed into the fourth and final IBC. Build a support system from wood to raise the IBC's about thirty inches to make storage under the IBC's. Under the IBC's will be stored a hose and other plumbing supplies.

Under the IBC's and garden, place a tarp to contain any water spillage. All told, you should have over 3,000 gallons {11,360 liters} of stored water (including the garden) (over 2,200 gallons {8,400 liters} of potable water) with the ability to replenish via the well, rainwater and pond. You could eventually increase the amount of water stored by adding more barrels and IBC's.

WATER USAGE FOR SHABBOS AND HOLIDAYS

THIS SMALL SECTION IS FOR Jews. Because the type of water system that will be employed, you will not have any issues with use of water on Shabbos or Jewish holidays. The temperature for the tank-less water heater is below *yad soledet bo* (114 degrees Fahrenheit) {45.6 degrees Celsius} and therefore not considered cooking. Check with your local *posek,* as there may still be a problem with *pesik riashah*. However, I suggest you use the stored water on these days to at least recycle some of the stored water over time. This is not necessary, but would be preferred. This would also be the case for the bathroom toilet water.

DRINKING WATER

FOR DRINKING WATER, KEEP SEVERAL water-filter type pitchers. Keep one in the fridge at all times and at least one on the shelves on both the main and bedroom levels. These containers must be kept full at all times.

The size of an IBC is 48" {122 centimeters} L x 40" {102 centimeters} W x 54" {137 centimeters} H, and hold about 330 gallons {1,250 liters} each. In addition to the IBC's, you will also have the ability to fill drinking water-filter pitchers, 7-gallon water totes, 1-gallon containers, fifty-five gallon water barrels and more. You will have over twenty filled fifty-five gallon water barrels in the bedroom, halls, decontamination and storage rooms for emergency use.

GRAY WATER

COLLECT ALL GRAY WATER FROM the washing machine and shower, and store it in storage area 68 to be used in the toilet. (For Jews: Due to *kosher* laws, you may only collect water from *parve* and meat OR dairy water. The other, should be dispose of directly down the toilet or preferably take it outside.)

NOTES

THE TANK-LESS WATER HEATER will only be turned on as needed for as short a period as possible, to conserve electricity. Keep the water temperature about 110 degrees Fahrenheit {43.3 degrees Celsius} to use just the water from the hot water pipe. Showers and dish washing will be timed to conserve electricity.

One possibility for an outdoor shower is:
http://www.nemoequipment.com/product/?p=Helio%20Pressure%20Shower

POND

MAKE a large pond, approximately fifty feet {fifteen meters} from the surface structure. The pond will help with the ecosystem. Depending on the property you purchase, you could try to set up the pond to be fed by a stream. The pond will be filled by rainwater, and additionally by the stream, if there is one. If it is set up correctly, the pond would offer you some protection on one side of the surface structure.

I suggest the pond be about four feet {1.2 meters} deep on the surface structure's side and maybe seven feet {2.1 meters} deep on the side away from the surface structure. The pond would be about fifteen feet {4.6 meters} wide and about one-hundred feet {30.5 meters} long. It would be far enough away from the bunker that it would not interfere with the structure, but close enough to be useful. Assuming the pond is completely filled with water, it would hold close to 62,000 gallons {234,700 liters} of water. There will be a four inch PVC pipe that would enable you to bring water from the pond into the bunker. This incoming water would enter the bunker via the ramp. There would be a shut-off valve on this pipe to prevent flooding. By doing this, you should have an unlimited supply of water. The PVC pipes would be buried at least eighteen inches deep and be insulated. The pipe would need to be below the local frost line to prevent freezing. For example, the mid-eastern seaboard region of the United States, the frost line is about eighteen inches.

Section off two small areas of the pond. One area, with a dam (set up to filter large debris), will be able to feed the bunker as needed. The second area will be set up to allow you to bathe and wash dishes. Instead of bathing and washing, you could put edible fish in the pond. Personally, I suggest putting fish in the pond and have the water available to help feed the hens and goats.

TIRE WALL

THIS is going to sound strange, even to a prepper, however, do some Internet searches and you will be surprised what you find. There are people, including a good friend of mine, who are making their entire bunkers out of tires. As I have mentioned, most people are not making their bunkers well enough to protect themselves. I suggest not making your bunker out of tires; however, I advocate making a surface wall and maybe even the surface structure out of tires. This chapter will describe what I mean.

The nice thing about tires is they are free. Most service stations pay $2 or $3 per tire to have them recycled. When you pick them up for free, the service stations are excited to save the money and the time it would take to transport the tires to the recycling plant. It does not matter what type of tires you get, or in what condition.

Dig a trench that is about as wide as your first layer of tires and the depth of one tire. Start laying out the tires in your trench. When you add the second layer of tires, take 1 to 1-1/2 inch screws and attach the tires together one on top of the other (this is not a requirement). Place some cardboard inside each tire and then fill them with dirt. It would be a good idea to have a few rocks to assist (two to four inches) in firming up the tire. The reason for the cardboard is to prevent the dirt from coming out of the bottom of the tire. In each tire, compress as much dirt as possible. Use a pickax to help lift the sidewall to get more dirt inside the tire. Pound the dirt tight with a sledge hammer to get more dirt into the sidewall. Make sure to get the dirt completely inside of the sidewalls of each tire. Interlace the tire wall levels for a strong support. This means to stack the tires as you would a brick wall - staggered.

Be careful as each tire will weigh over 300 pounds {136 kilos}. I suggest you build your tire wall about seven to eight feet {2.5 meters} tall. Feel free to curve or angle the wall to suit your needs. Fill any gaps in your wall between tires with mortar or cement. Put razor wire on the top of the tire wall.

Use a level to make sure your wall is level. The concern is the sidewalls should be level from one tire to the next.

As noted above, you can also make the surface structure out of tires.

SECURITY

THE following is a run-down of the security I suggest you have in place for your property. I will break this up by area to make it easier to plan and implement. Much of the information delineated below has already been mentioned in other chapters, however, I wanted to have everything in one place to make it more comprehensive and give you more details.

Some of things you are going to do are only going to make your property **look** very protected. An intruder or marauder will see you are protected and secure and probably say to themselves they should find another place that is an easier target. That being said, most of your security will be real and cause actual physical injury if traversed.

WEAPONS

LEARN ARCHERY AND HOW TO shoot a firearm. Learn martial arts. Stock up with firearms and ammunition. Get a large dog.

Make sure you get all appropriate licenses and permits for your location and the type of weapons you are stocking. I suggest you stock up on several different types of firearms.

You will want hand guns and shotguns. You will need to make sure you are well stocked with as much ammunition as possible. Hide a variety of weapons around your compound and bunker.

Also, get cross bows, and plenty of arrows. Other weapons you should consider are; tasers, knives, stun guns, flare guns, swords, axes, mace or pepper spray. Almost anything can be a weapon. Your best weapon is your mind. Fights are won more by brains than brawn.

DRIVEWAY

AS MENTIONED, MAKE THE DRIVEWAY narrow to allow only one vehicle passage at a time. On either side of the driveway put heavy logs and boulders. Make the driveway into an "S" curve to prevent someone from driving straight across your property. Put IR sensors across your driveway to alert you of someone's presence.

PROPERTY

YOU WILL HAVE EXTENSIVE SECURITY around the property and the security will get tighter and more extensive as one gets closer to the compound.

Around the edge of your property, ideally you should put some fencing; however, this may be impractical as the size of your property will be quite large. On the other hand, you may be able to put some fencing at strategic points on the edge of your property with some barbed wire on top. In addition, put some "Posted" or "Private Property" signs strategically. http://www.walmart.com/c/kp/no-trespassing-signs

I am conflicted with the following, but I will share it with you. You may want to consider putting a surveillance camera at the driveway by the entrance to your property. This does not necessarily need to be a working camera, just something to show an intruder they may be under

WWW.DOOMSDAYBUNKERBOOK.COM

observation. However, this will give passersby knowledge that someone may be here. On the other hand, it may scare intruders away with the knowledge they are being watched. Now you can see my struggle with this issue.

Mark trees to show you where it is safe to travel in several different directions. For underground traps, consider keeping them covered for your own protection until you encounter a SHTF scenario, then uncover all the traps and move inside the bunker and do not come back out until it is safe.

BOOBY-TRAPS

SET UP BOOBY-TRAPS AROUND the property to protect yourselves from intruders. Some ideas are in the following chart. Have several of each of these traps.

D = Deadly	M = Maim

BATTERING RAMS	If someone trips a trigger line, it releases a heavy log that will cut down an intruder. If you put sharp sticks into the battering ram, it could kill.	D
BEAR TRAP	You can purchase bear traps and deploy them as desired.	M
DOOR TRAP	Two lengths of bamboo with the cross section heavily spiked and suspended above a door or opening via a trip wire. When the wire is tripped the trap swings down impaling the victim.	D
ELECTRIC FENCE	Electrify your fences, both around the compound and the edge of your property. Post signs accordingly.	M
FISHING HOOKS	Hang fishing hooks from fishing wire in the trees. This way, if someone walks through them, they will get cut	M

MACE TRAP	Mace traps take various forms, and may consist of a spiked concrete ball, drum, box or log suspended in a tree on the end of a rope, or cable. When the trip wire is pulled, the mace swings down along the path striking anyone in its way.	D
PILL BOXES	Described below	
RAZOR WIRE	Put razor wire several places around the property and compound. In order to protect yourself from the razor wire, put some chicken wire on the inside of it.	M
SPIKE BOARD	The spike board is used with a pit and consists of a treadle board, one end of which is spiked. When someone steps on the treadle, the spiked end flies up striking him in the face or chest.	D
TRENCHES	Dig trenches in the ground and camouflage them. Make them in the same way as vaults, but longer.	M
TRIP LINES	Place fishing line wires about six inches {15.2 centimeters} off the ground so an intruder will trip	M
UNDERGROUND TRAPS	Dig holes in the ground. If someone stepped in them, they would possibly break a leg.	M
VAULTS	Dig deep holes in the ground and camouflage them so someone will fall into them. Consider putting them after the trip lines. Make the holes deep and spike them with steaks so if someone falls into them, they will be severely hurt.	M

PILL BOX

Make a few "pill box's" around the property. Dig a pit about three feet {.9 meters} deep, five feet {1.5 meters} long and about four feet {1.2 meters} wide. Place a few rows of cinder blocks in front and bent at an angle a bit to the sides (___/ upside down), with a hole for a gun. Have a fake rifle propped inside to scare intruders. Have these partially camouflaged to give the impression you are trying to hide them. Fill the empty space of the cinder blocks with cement.

COMPOUND

PLACE BARBED WIRE CHAIN LINK fencing around the area of your property you want to have most secured. We will call this area the compound. This area will house the surface structure, bunker, hens, goats and more. Build a six foot {1.8 meters} tall fence and top it with razor wire. Add an additional coil of razor wire (Star of David) on the ground inside the fence. If someone is able to get over the fence, they would land on the second razor wire. Put chicken wire on the inside of the Star of David to protect yourselves and pets from accidental contact. You should electrify the fence.

TIRE WALL

Make a tire wall on one edge of the compound and put razor wire on top. Make the tire wall eight feet {2.5 meters} tall. When building the tire wall, stagger the tires away from the surface structure about an inch per level. This will make it more difficult for an intruder to climb.

POND

Make a large pond, maybe fifty feet {fifteen meters} or so from the surface structure. The pond could offer you some protection on the one side of the compound. Make the pond about four feet {1.2 meters} deep on the bunker's side and maybe seven feet {2.1 meters} deep on the side away from the surface structure. The pond would be about fifteen feet {4.6 meters} wide and about one-hundred feet {30.5 meters} long. On the bottom of the deep end of the pond, put razor wire, so if someone does go into the pond, they would be cut by the razor wire. Put some of chicken wire on your side of the razor wire for your own protection.

Any time you are out of the bunker, but still on your property, carry weapons. Hide a few cans of pepper spray around the property and compound. Always have your dog with you when you are inside **and** outside of the bunker.

Get a DIY (Do It Yourself) drone to have an aerial view of the area. This will give you an idea as to what is going on, who is in the area and what roads are clear. You would also have an idea as to where other people may be who can help you or need your help. It would also give you advanced warning of invasion. http://diydrones.com/

On the four corners of the surface structure and in the trees, put up at least six to nine video cameras for surveillance. Depending on the location of the emergency exit, maybe put one of the video cameras by the rear hatch.

In some of the trees, put up loud speakers near the extremes of the compound area. Have the speakers wired into the bunker. If you see someone crossing onto your property, you can make an announcement that the area is secure and they are being watched. Hopefully, this will deter any intruder.

COMPOUND LIGHTING

YOU WILL WANT TO PUT some lights in the compound area. The following is what I recommend:

Put one of these on each of the corners and along the fence of the compound:

http://www.homedepot.com/p/Defiant-180-Degree-Outdoor-Motion-Activated-White-LED-Security-Floodlight-MST18920LWDF/203303763?N=5yc1vZc7qf.

These lights should be pointing away from the compound toward the property in order to keep you in the dark and clearly show any intruders.

Put one of these by each corner of the surface structure and one near the hens and another by the goats:

http://www.homedepot.com/p/Defiant-180-Degree-Outdoor-Black-Motion-Sensing-Security-Light-DF-5416-BK/203716689?N=5yc1vZc7qfZ1z0sk0s.

These are for your own lighting and should be off if an intruder comes along.

SURFACE STRUCTURE

ON THE SURFACE, OVER THE front entrance of the bunker, have a surface structure with some supplies as a diversion just in case you are attacked. The attacker can have the few cans of food and about 100 gallons {379 liters} of water you keep in the surface structure. Do not keep anything of value in the surface structure.

If you are going to use a shed as your surface structure, fill the walls of the shed with sand and small stones to insulate and protect from gunfire. Attach to the studs 3/4" plywood. Fill the space behind the plywood with sand and 1/2" - 3/4" stones. This sand will protect you from most gunfire and will also insulate the shed from cold. Pour the sand and stones for the bottom six feet {1.8 meters} and use regular insulation above that, if needed. On the inside of the 3/4" plywood, attach sheet metal to add more protection from gunfire.

Bullet-proof the windows and electrify the front door of the surface structure.

Put some bubble wrap on the floor so it will make a loud noise when someone is there and warn you of their presence.

If you use a tire structure, you do not need to put sand in the walls.

FRONT ENTRANCE

THE FRONT HATCH WILL BE a thirty-two inch {eighty-one centimeters} by thirty-eight inch {one meter} flat blast hatch built into concrete under the floor of the surface structure. Weld to the hatch sheet metal brackets to support a bar to prevent someone from invading. Get an electromagnetic locking system for more security.

Booby-trap the entrance. For the booby-trap, have a car battery hooked to a plate on the ramp so when someone steps on it, they will get shocked. Have a kill-switch hidden in the wall closer to the decontamination room.

Put some bubble wrap on the floor. It makes a loud noise when someone steps on it and will scare the intruder and warn you of their presence.

At the bottom of the ramp have an exterior steel door (door 3) that will lead to the decontamination room. Put a barricade on the inside of the door to prevent ingress from intruders. Also, consider electrifying the door.

The door leading into the bunker itself (door 4) will be an exterior steel door that will be well insulated. Put a barricade on the inside of the door to prevent ingress from intruders.

BUNKER

THE ENTIRE STRUCTURE WILL BE four inch poured, concrete. The roof of the bunker will be ten feet {30.5

centimeters} below the surface. You will be well hidden and secure. No one should be able to find you. With the walls of the bunker so thick and strong, you will not have to be concerned with intruders demolishing the bunker. However, you will have weapons to help protect you from any intruders who may manage to get to the actual bunker. You should have firearms, ammunition, knives, tasers, pepper spray, flare guns and more. You will also have your dog with you in the bunker.

REAR EXIT

The emergency exit will have a hatch that will be the same as the front (door 2) except it will be thirty-two inches by thirty-two inches {eighty-one centimeters by eighty-one centimeters }. Get an electromagnetic locking system for more security. Electrify the hatch.

Booby-trap the emergency exit. For the booby-trap, have a car battery hooked up to a plate on the ramp so when someone steps on it, they will get shocked. Have a kill-switch hidden in the wall close to the bunker. Put a taut mono-filament fishing wire across the ramp about six inches from the floor so an intruder will trip.

Put some bubble wrap on the floor. When someone steps on it, the bubble wrap will make a loud noise and will scare the intruder and warn you of their presence.

Make sure to camouflage the emergency exit very well as there will be no shed above. I am more concerned with the security of the emergency exit than I am with the main entrance, as the emergency exit will not be as well hidden. Have the hatch buried under a foot or two of dirt.

The door leading from the bunker to the ramp (door 8) will be an exterior steel door that will be well insulated. Put bars on the inside of the door to prevent ingress from intruders. This door will only be used in the case of emergency. Consider electrifying this door.

HEATING & COOLING

THE ambient temperature in your bunker should be approximately fifty-five degrees. Get a wood pellet stove for heating. The pellet stove should bring the temperature to seventy degrees Fahrenheit {21.2 degrees Celsius} with very little effort or expenditure. The stove itself should cost under $2,000. Since there is no insulation problems with solid concrete and being so far underground, the inside temperature should be fairly constant and not take much, in the way of the pellets, to heat and maintain the temperature.

Get a pellet stove vacuum to clean out the ash. The ash can be used in the composting pit and the toilet.

Wood pellets will be stored in storage area 81.

To have a place to burn your paper and cardboard trash, also have a wood burning stove. Time your burning in the wood stove for cooking and shower times.

http://www.homedepot.com/p/US-Stove-900-sq-ft-Wood-Burning-Stove-1261/202245276?MERCH=REC-_-product-

3-_-203630368-_-202245276-_-N#product_description
$375

In the vent from the wood stove, have a fan to exhaust the bunker in the case of internal smoke or other emergency.

The pipes from both stoves will go straight up and through the ceiling in order to deliver some heat to the bedroom.

FLOWER POT HEATER

CAN YOU IMAGINE HEATING A small area with just a candle? Not only can you imagine it, I will show you how to make it happen. Keep this in storage area 111.

> Purchase a ten to twelve inch {25.4 - 30.5 centimeter} flower pot (with no hole in the bottom), three bricks, a small plate and some candles. Arrange the bricks to support the flower pot when it is placed upside down on them. Leave some space between the bricks so the candle can breathe. Place the plate between the bricks. Light the candle and adhere it to the plate. Place a few ounces of water on the plate for safety purposes (for when the candle burns down). Cover the candle with the flower pot.
>
> The candle will breathe because of the space between the bricks. The flower pot will heat up and provide heat long after the candle goes out.

AIR CONDITIONING

There will be no need for cooling in your bunker. However, the following is instructions to make an air conditioner for the surface structure, outside or even the root cellar.

> Purchase a five gallon {nineteen liter} bucket with lid. Find a Styrofoam insert that is a tight fit. Also needed are three - 1 1/4" PVC pipes that are about three inches long, a low powered fan that will fit in the lid of

the bucket and some glue.

In the side of the bucket cut three holes (a few inches apart) about six inches from the top that continues through the Styrofoam insert. Insert the PVC pipes into the holes and seal with glue. Cut a hole in the top of the bucket so the fan will be able to lay down on top, pointing in, and be supported by the bucket lid. Inside the bucket, place either a jug of ice or just dump a bunch of ice into the insert. Do NOT use dry ice, as a bi-product of the melting dry ice is CO_2.

COMMAND CENTER

THE command center is a place where you can monitor what is going on outside your bunker, the weather, news, security and more. Personally, I recommend having your office at this location as this is probably where you will be for a good part of your day.

In order to be in touch with other people in the case of a SHTF scenario, get a Ham radio license and a 2mm radio. Put an antenna outside. Follow the rules and laws of the FCC.

If you do not have a Ham radio license, get a short-wave radio to be able to monitor the Ham bands.

Several other things to have in the command center: Surveillance monitoring system, drone control and monitoring, weather station, one of the walkie-talkies. I also suggest having a faraday cage in your command center.

SHELVES

I have spent considerable time delving into where I think certain things should go in the bunker. If you would like my complete list, please go to my website www.doomsdaybunkerbook.com. The list will include additional, more detailed drawings showing where the shelves should go.

I am not going to convert this chapter to metric as shelving units in different areas and countries will be different.

I am figuring ninety-two shelving units. The length of each shelf is forty-eight inches. Total shelf length = 368' X 2' X 5 shelves = 3,680 SF of shelves. Use some shelf makers and drawers to make extra storage. When first building the shelves, start with the bottom shelf and top shelf. Attach the other shelves as needed for the space.

Most book shelves will be about twelve inches tall.

Edsal brand 48 inch wide x 72 inch tall x 24 inch deep, steel commercial shelving unit. $80 each at Home Depot. Five shelves per unit. Raise them up as necessary on bricks. These units give more shelves for about the same price as the ones you could make from wood, and they take up less space.

92 Shelving Units $80@ = $7,360

Several of the shelving units may need to be made by hand.

Put cube crates on the top of the fridge and freezer. Make shelves above the washing machine and doors. Also put cube crates around the perimeter of the bedroom level.

A few of the shelving units should be on casters: 58 & 59.

In the basement level hall behind the stairs, have additional storage.

In the bedroom hall, you can build a platform over the stairs and use that for additional storage.

SOLAR PANEL SYSTEM

WATCH the YouTube video of LDS Prepper for information on how to make this whole thing for under $5,000. Get extra fuses. The inside components of the system will be in storage area 44 inside a faraday cage. During construction, have a grounding rod installed. The size of a solar panel is 2"X39"X77".

Resources: www.backwoodssolar.com
www.wholesalesolar.com

The following chart would generate about 1KW per day. You would need to at least double and preferably triple this system ($15,000) to comfortably live off the grid and give you 3KW per day of electricity. I also suggest you purchase extra panels so if there is an EMP or something else happens to your solar panels, you will have backup.

PART	#	WEBSITE
Grape Solar 280 watt Solar Panel	4	http://www.amazon.com/Grape-Solar-GS-P-280-Fab1-280-Watt-Polycrystalline/dp/B00635XSEG/ref=sr_1_1?ie=UTF8&qid=1383451304&sr=8-1&keywords=Grape+solar+GS-P-280-fab1+280+watt

BZ 500 MPPT Watt PV Charge Controller	2	http://www.bzproducts.net/id2.html
6 volt Rayovac Ultra Pro Golf Car Batteries	12	http://www.batteriesplus.com/product /33332-SLIGC110-6-volt-Battery/574-SLI/6067-Golf-Cart-Batteries/133277-E--Z--GO/TXT/TXT.aspx
Samlex 24 Volt 1500 Watt Pure Sine Inverter	1	http://www.amazon.com/gp/product/ B003FWNWWI/ref=as_li_ss_tl?ie=U TF8&camp=1789&creative=390957& creativeASIN=B003FWNWWI&linkC ode=as2&tag=yt0c-20
Batter Tender 24 Volt Battery Charger	1	http://www.amazon.com/gp/product/ B002DTV172/ref=as_li_ss_tl?ie=UTF 8&camp=1789&creative=390957&cr eativeASIN=B002DTV172&linkCode =as2&tag=yt0c-20
Battery Saver Desulfator	1	http://www.amazon.com/gp/product/ B003Z3EZ1O/ref=as_li_ss_tl?ie=UT F8&camp=1789&creative=390957&c reativeASIN=B003Z3EZ1O&linkCode =as2&tag=yt0c-20
24" Starter to switch Battery Cable	13	http://www.amazon.com/gp/product/ B000BPTUFK/ref=as_li_ss_tl?ie=UT F8&camp=1789&creative=390957&c reativeASIN=B000BPTUFK&linkCod e=as2&tag=yt0c-20
6 AWG Multi Strand Copper Wire 60'	4	http://www.amazon.com/gp/product/ B003HGHQT2/ref=as_li_ss_tl?ie=UT F8&camp=1789&creative=390957&c reativeASIN=B003HGHQT2&linkCod e=as2&tag=yt0c-20
4'X8' 1/2" Plywood for Battery Box	1	
Wire Nuts, Zip Ties, etc		
35 watt fuses	2	In-line

200 Watt Fuse w/ holder	1	http://www.amazon.com/mn/search/?_encoding=UTF8&camp=1789&creative=390957&field-keywords=anl%20fuse&linkCode=ur2&sprefix=anl%2Caps%2C175&tag=yt0c-20&url=search-alias%3Daps
Kill A Watt	2	http://www.p3international.com/products/p4400.html
2X4 Lumber		To build support frame

A more detailed chart is available for free on the website.

Use the following information to help determine your power needs. As an analogy, we will use a garden hose with a water flow to help us understand electrical terms.

CURRENT

ELECTRICAL CURRENT MEASURES THE RATE of flow of electrons in a circuit and is measured in **Amps**. In a water analogy, it is the flow rate of water.

VOLTAGE

VOLTAGE MEASURES THE AMOUNT OF electrical potential. In our water analogy, it is a measure of how much water pressure you have. For most applications, voltage does not change. Common voltages for emergency power systems are 220/240, 110/120, 24, 12, and 6. Household voltage is 110/120 in the United States.

POWER

POWER IS HOW MUCH ELECTRICITY you have used. When you see **Watts** or **VA** on an appliance tag, it is talking about **Power**. In our water analogy, think of the total volume of water transferred.

OHM'S LAW

A GENTLEMAN NAMED GEORG OHM discovered a relationship between these three (power, voltage and current) measurements. Nowadays we call this **Ohm's** Law. Simply put, the equation is $P = VI$. In non algebraic terms, it means ***Power = Voltage X Current***. The main thing to take away from this is for any given load, as you reduce voltage your current increases.

PUTTING IT ALL TOGETHER

IF YOU HAVE AN APPLIANCE that uses 1100 **watts** of **power** at 110V it will pull 10 **Amps** of **Current**. If you run it off an inverter hooked up to a 12V battery, it will pull a whopping 91 Amps.

In our water analogy, think of your common 1/2″ garden hose. The water pressure (**Voltage**) does not change. If we use a stopwatch and calculate how much time it takes us to fill a five gallon bucket, you get a rate of water flow (**Current**). If you swap that hose for a 1″ diameter hose and measure the fill time, you will find out your water flow rate (**Current**) has changed even though pressure at the spigot (**Voltage**) and the size of the bucket (**Power**) have not changed at all.

(Wattage × Hours Used Per Day) ÷ 1000 = Daily Kilowatt-hour (kWh) consumption

1 kilowatt (kW) = 1,000 Watts

Multiply this by the number of days you use the appliance during the year for the annual consumption in kWh per year.

That said, let us take a very simple system to make it easier to understand. Let us say we want to run a Crockpot for ten hours a day, have some twenty-four hour lighting available, and a bit extra just in case. All run off the battery storage system which is replenished from a generator.

The first piece of information we need is how much power these things use. This is easy if we are provided with the power draw by the manufacturer. If the manufacturer only provides us with current draw, then we just calculate the power.

For lighting, let us figure we want ten bulbs. If you buy CFLs you can get the equivalent of a 100W incandescent bulb that uses only 23W. So for lighting, your overall power usage is 230W for the ten bulbs. Realistically you will not have them all on at once, but let us be conservative and say you will.

Unfortunately the Crockpot does not tell us how much power it uses, but it does say that at 120V it will use 2A. Since we know P = VI, we can calculate the used power as 120V X 2A = 240W.

NOTE: *Battery storage capacity is measured in something called Reserve Capacity* (RC) *and is defined as the length of time in minutes the battery can power a 25A load without the available voltage dropping too low.*

Since we know how long we want to power these loads, we can calculate the amount of reserve capacity we need for each load. The formula used for this is *RC (in minutes) = Run Time (in hours) X Wattage / 4.545* (the 4.545 is a conversion factor, just in case you were wondering.)

Lighting: 24 hours X 230W / 4.545 = 1215

Crockpot: 10 hours X 240W / 4.545 = 1268

Total RC Required: 1215 + 1268 = 2483 minutes

If we get a bunch of 12V batteries with an RC of 200 each, we will need thirteen batteries total. As always, we want to buffer this a bit, so call it fifteen batteries. Even a small system as we have outlined will have a very large footprint and start getting expensive.

To keep the batteries charged, we will want a trickle charger to keep them topped off. We will need to have a power inverter to convert the DC power of the batteries into AC power our appliances can use. Power inverters have an input voltage (in this case we want 12V DC) and an output voltage (in this case we want 120V AC) and are rated for certain loads. Generally speaking, inverter specifications talk about peak and sustain loads, and are measured in watts. In our case, we need an inverter capable of at least 500W (230W + 240W). It would be better to get one that is larger.

CLOUDY DAYS

SOME COMMON QUESTIONS ARE, WHAT happens if there is a cloudy day? Will the solar panels work? Will the batteries charge?

The answer is yes, with a caveat. Because of the efficiency of modern day solar systems, you will be able to generate electricity on cloudy days. However, since it is not a sunny day, they will only work to about fifty percent, depending on how overcast the day.

AVERAGE WATTAGE CHART

THE following chart is a list of some appliances and their wattage. This chart is just for reference and not to be relied upon in every circumstance. Check your own appliances for exact wattage. This chart looks horrible in the book, however, there is a better looking version on the website for free.

100 Watt Incan. Bulb	100	Hair Dryer	1K	Range	5K
Baseboard Heater	1,600	Heating Blanket	200	Room A/C Unit	1,100
Blender	300	Heating Pad	65	Room Heater	1,350
Box Fan	175	Hot Plate	1200	Satellite Dish	30
Ceiling Fan	100	Humidifier	600	Sewing Machine	75
Cell Phone Charger	4	Iron	1,100	Shaver	15
Central Air Conditioner	5,000	Laptop	100	Sink Waste Disposal	450

CFL Bulb (100-Watt)	30	Microwave Oven	1,200	Stereo	1,200
Clock Radio	25	Mixer	130	Television	150
Clothes Dryer	4,900	Oven	8,000	Toaster	1,150
Coffee Maker	1,300	Popcorn Popper	1,400	Toaster Oven	1,150
Computer	300	Portable Fan	100	Two Burner Hot Plate	1,650
Dehumidifier	350			Vacuum Cleaner	1,350
Dishwasher	1,200			Washing Machine	500
Electric Blanket	200			Water Heater	200
Electric Clothes Dryer	3,400			Waterpik	100
Food Processor	200			Well Pump	500
Frost-Free Freezer	500				
Frost-Free Refrigerator	615				
Furnace	500				
Garbage Disposal	750				

TV's, computers, chargers, VCR's and many other devices left plugged in, but not turned on, still draw power. When not in use, unplug everything. By keeping electronic devices unplugged, you have the advantage of additional protection from EMP's (see later in this book).

To estimate the number of hours a refrigerator actually operates at its maximum wattage, divide the total time the refrigerator is plugged in by three. Refrigerators, although turned "on" all the time, actually cycle on and off as needed to maintain internal temperatures.

LOAD EVALUATION CHART

USE the following chart to understand **your** total electrical use. Note which loads are AC and which are DC. This, along with the largest AC load number, will help you pick an inverter to power your loads. Do not forget to include anticipated loads you would want to use in the future.

This estimate does not have to be EXACT. However, the closer you get, the better you will be able to design your solar system. It will be easier if you have done your homework in advance and have these numbers to assist you.

When doing calculations, figure in a loss factor of 0.8 as there are inefficiencies and losses in solar systems and batteries.

LOAD EVALUATION CHART

Appliance	AC	DC	QTY.	X	Wattage	X	Hours Per Day	X	Days Per Week	Divide by 7	=	Watt Hours Per Day
				X		X		X		/7	=	
				X		X		X		/7	=	
				X		X		X		/7	=	
				X		X		X		/7	=	
				X		X		X		/7	=	
				X		X		X		/7	=	
				X		X		X		/7	=	
				X		X		X		/7	=	
				X		X		X		/7	=	
				X		X		X		/7	=	
				X		X		X		/7	=	
				X		X		X		/7	=	
				X		X		X		/7	=	
				X		X		X		/7	=	
				X		X		X		/7	=	
				X		X		X		/7	=	
				X		X		X		/7	=	
				X		X		X		/7	=	
				X		X		X		/7	=	
				X		X		X		/7	=	
				X		X		X		/7	=	
				X		X		X		/7	=	
				X		X		X		/7	=	
				X		X		X		/7	=	
				X		X		X		/7	=	
				X		X		X		/7	=	
				X		X		X		/7	=	
TOTAL WATT HOURS PER DAY					X 0.8					**ACTUAL WATT HOURS PER DAY**		

DEVICES REQUIRING ELECTRICITY

THE following chart lists the electric devices you may have in your bunker. These are the devices I will have in my bunker. I made this list to assist you in your calculations.

Item	#	Hours	Watts	Watts/Day (kWh)
42" LCD TV	1	1	200	200
Air Filter Fan 3 watt	6	24	72	432
Air Filter Fan 3 watt	2	0		
Ceiling Fan	1		25	
Crock Pot	1	0	200	
Deep Fryer	1	0	1,200	
Dish Receiver	1	15	30	450
Food Processor	1	0	350	
Freezer	1	8	300	2,400
Garden (including timers)				
Lights	4	16	68	1,088
Water Pumps	2	24	5	120
Air Pump	2	24	5	120
Griddle	1	0	1,200	
Heating Blanket	1	0	60	

DEVICES REQUIRING ELECTRICITY

Device	Qty			
Hot Plate	1	.167	1,200	200
Hot Water Heater	1	.25	300	75
Laptop Computers	2	16	100	1,600
LCD Monitor (TV)	1	15	75	1,125
Lights	1	16	17	272
Microwave	1	.25	1200	300
Pellet Stove	1			
Printer	2		90	
Radon Fan	1			
Refrigerator	1	8	110	880
Router	1	15	24	360
Security System	1			
Small Refrigerator	1	8		400
Stereo	1	12	40	480
Stink Fan	1	24	5	120
Stove	1			
Sump Pump	1		100	
Toaster Oven	1	0	1000	
Washing Machine	1	.25	300	75
Water Pump	1			

For lighting, use only LED lights. LED bulbs use the least amount of electricity and will last the longest.

Consider using power strips and extension cords for power distribution throughout the bunker.

ELECTRICAL CIRCUIT CHART

THERE will be a four inch hole in the floor of the bedroom and main level at about twelve O'clock to the left of the door, in order to facilitate the power cables going to the different levels. The numbers next to the "light" refer to the storage areas in the bunker.

	LOCATION	BULB WATTAGE	WIRING
1	Decontamination room	10	Power strip
2	Front ramp	5	
3	Sump pump		
4	Bedroom	5	Power strip
5	Sofa lamp	21	
6	27 light	21	
7	20-23 light	10	
8	Bedroom hall light, water pump	10	
9	Garden	4X21	Power strip
10	Entertainment center		Power strip
11	Pellet stove		
12	LR light, game table	21	
13	Office light	21	
14	Office outlet		Power strip

15	Washing machine		Power strip
16	Fridge		
17	Stove		
18	Kitchen light	21	
19	DR light	21	
20	Main hall	10	
21	Bathroom light	10	
22	Tank-less water heater		
23	Back ramp	5	
24	81-120 light	10	
25	110-115 light	10	
26	98-104 light	10	
27	87-92 light	10	
28	71-85 light	10	
29	Storage hall light	10	
30	Radon fan		If needed
31	Freezer		Extension cord

RADON

RADON is a cancer-causing radioactive gas. You cannot see, smell or taste radon, but it may be a problem in your bunker. I have never seen any bunker design take this into consideration. The Surgeon General has warned that radon is the second leading cause of lung cancer in the United States today. If you smoke and your home has high radon levels, you are at a very high risk for developing lung cancer. Some scientific studies of radon exposure indicate that children may be more sensitive to radon. This may be due to their higher respiration rate and their rapidly dividing cells, which may be more vulnerable to radiation damage.

Testing is the only way to know your bunker's radon levels. There are no immediate symptoms that will alert you to the presence of radon. It typically takes years of exposure before any problems surface.

I suggest installing a passive radon reduction system. This will set in place a system to passively mitigate radon, and other earth gasses, from the bunker and also have the availability to install a fan, if needed, at a later date. It would be much less expensive and easier to prepare the system in advance, than to install a system at a later date.

This passive system does not require energy or fans to move the radon and air. This system will reduce soil gas entry and include piping to vent the gases outdoors. This system should cost about $1000. The basic components are as follows:

1. **GAS PERMEABLE LAYER OF AGGREGATE**. This layer is placed under the foundation slab of the bunker. This is done to allow the soil gas to move freely underneath the bunker and enter an exhaust pipe. It is recommended to use a six to eight inch layer of clean 1/2" - 3/4" gravel.

2. **PERFORATED PVC PIPE**. From about twelve inches in from the edge of the bunker, and throughout the aggregate, lay four inch PVC perforated pipe. Connect all the pipes with plumbers glue. These pipes have two sets of perforations running the length of the pipe, ninety degrees from each other. Make sure one set of the perforations from each pipe are pointing down to avoid any moisture accumulating which will lead to mold.

3. **PLASTIC SHEETING / SOIL GAS RETARDER**. This is the primary soil / gas barrier and serves to support any cracks that may form after the basement slab is cured. It is usually made of six mil polyethylene sheeting, overlapped twelve inches at the seams and fitted closely around all pipe, wire, or other penetrations. It is placed over the gas permeable layer of clean aggregate. Also use sealing tape at all overlapping areas of the plastic sheeting.

4. **SEALING AND CAULKING.** Sealing and caulking all openings in the concrete foundation floor will reduce soil gas entry into the bunker. A polyurethane or silicone caulk should be used.

5. **PVC VENT PIPE.** A vertical PVC vent pipe of four inch diameter will be connected to a vent pipe "T"

which is installed below the slab in the aggregate. This "T" will be at nine O'clock in the foundation. The vent pipe runs from the gas permeable layer (where the "T" is located) up through the bunker to the surface to safely vent radon and other soil gases. On each floor of the bunker, the pipe should be labeled, "Radon Reduction System".

6. In the future, if there is a need for a fan, it can easily be installed in the bedroom level of the bunker.

7. Even if there is no need for a radon remediation system, I still recommend you leave this pipe unsealed so any soil gasses will be able to be vented to the surface.

8. Put a blast valve on the end of this pipe.

Radon testing kit:
http://www.amazon.com/First-Alert-RD1-Radon-Test/dp/B00002N83E/ref=sr_1_1/184-7040453-7397635?ie=UTF8&qid=1396155592&sr=8-1&keywords=radon+testing+kit

PIPE CHART

THIS chart is an approximation and you will need to find the lengths and sizes based on your specific setup.

Item	Length	Dia	Segments	Material
Air	80'	4"	2	PVC
Cables	10'	4"		PVC
Down Spouts	20'		2	
FPT Ball Valve		1"	3	PVC
FPT Ball Valve		4"	10	PVC
Flexible Hose		4"	2	
Garden				PVC
Gutter Guards	48'		17	
IBC Water		4"		PVC
Misc Adapters				
Pipe Caps		4"		PVC
Radon Pipe	110'	4"	5	PVC
Rain Gutters	48'		5	
Stink Pipe	60'	1"	2	PVC
T Pipe		4"		PVC
T Pipe		1"	3	PVC

T Pipe		4"	2		Aluminum
Vent (2)		4"	2		Aluminum
Water	40'	1"			PVC & Hose
Y tube into PVC		4"	1		PVC

In the "cables" pipe would be the following cables: 4 long extension cords (two coming into the bunker and two going out from the bunker), video monitor cables, FM antenna, solar power cables, GPS wire, Dish Network, speaker wire and extra unused wires. Seal this pipe on both ends. Color-code the extra unused wires for differentiation. You do not need pipe in the ramp for the cables.

Your specific designs will vary from this chart; however, this will give you a good starting point.

Use Dish Network for both cable TV and Internet

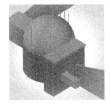

TOILET

IN many of the bunker designs I have seen, this is woefully under developed. Off the main level at the hall area, by storage area 64, is the bathroom. This toilet will empty into a surface level septic system. Used water from the shower and washing machine will be used to feed the toilet. Keep a fifty-five gallon barrel of gray water by storage area 68 for this purpose.

The septic tank and leach field will be much higher than the bunker. In fact, it will have to be close to the surface in order to be able to be serviced. In order to get the water up from the toilet to the septic tank, you will need a macerator and pump. This is what I recommend:

http://www.saniflo.com/homeowners/sfa-product-line/adaptable-grinders-and-lift-stations-for-small-spaces-and-commercial-buildings/

Off the side of the bunker by storage area 67, make a pit that is outside, for a composting pit. This pit will be used for organic waste in the time of a SHTF. This pit should be six feet deep by at least six feet by six feet {1.8 meters L,W,H} (216 CF {6.1 cubic meter}). It will be accessed by a hatch in the wall.

Have a stink pipe (one inch PVC) from both the toilet and composting pit that goes to the surface. Try to configure the pipes to be closed off if necessary. This will probably have to be done at the surface. A blast valve may be sufficient.

Have kitty litter and sawdust on hand to help with the smell and composting. Have a way to stir the compost once a week, and once a year or less often to clean out some of the compost. Any organic material may be put into the composting pit.

Build some narrow shelves in the bathroom, maybe put a cosmetic mirror on one of the shelves.

Make a composting pit outside the surface structure. This will be for use before SHTF. The outdoor composting pit should be about nine square feet {3 square meter}.

http://www.omick.net/composting_toilets/barrel_toilet.htm

WASTE MANAGEMENT

RECYCLE and reuse as much of everything as possible.

	BEFORE TSHTF	AFTER TSHTF
CARDBOARD	Wood stove	Wood stove
DOG WASTE	Toilet	Toilet / composting pit
EXCREMENT	Toilet	Toilet / composting pit
GLASS	Recycle facility	Trash tube
METALS	Recycle facility	Compact and then trash tube
ORGANIC	Outside composting pit or animal feed	Composting pit
PAPER	Wood stove	Wood stove
PLASTIC	Recycle facility	Compact and then trash tube
URINE	Toilet	Toilet / composting pit
WATER	Reuse water into the toilet	Reuse water into the toilet
WOOD	Wood stove	Wood stove

Trash compactor:

http://www.frontgate.com/stainless-steel-manual-trash-compactor/kitchen-entertaining/kitchen-storage-maintenance/543613?redirect=y $200.

The trash compactor will be by storage area 67.

In the main hall by the stairs going down to the basement (on the outside wall), about three feet {one meter} up, make a trash tube to the outside. This tube would be four feet by four feet {1.2 X 1.2 meters} and at least ten feet {three meters} long with an open end or hole. 160 CF {4.3 cubic meters}. The trash tube would angle down about ten to fifteen degrees. Put a door with a seal on the opening to keep the smells in the tube. However, there would likely not be any smells as all organic waste would be disposed of in the composting pit. Before putting anything in the trash tube, put it in the compactor. The trash tube will be made out of steel. Make a stink pipe leading to the surface.

Also off the bathroom about three feet {one meter} from the floor on the outside wall, make a composting pit opening. This pit should be 6'X6'X6'. The door of the composting pit should be able to give a solid seal and be at the top of the composting pit. This would also be outside.

The septic tank will be at least 1000 gallon {3,785 liter}. 1000 gal heavy duty 96"L x 78"W x 61"H

The leach field should be 8' X 100' {2.4 X 30.5 meters}.

FOOD

THERE are a number of things you can do to ensure you will have adequate food stored. Since you will have a decent amount of land, consider raising hens, chickens, goats, honeybees and rabbits for food. You should also learn how to hunt deer for meat. If you are Jewish, learn the laws of ritual slaughter and related topics.

Store food as follows:

Food	3, 9, 14, 61-68, 72-78
Kitchen Appliances	6, 71
Seasonings	69
Condiments	79

Learn how to can food, and can as much as possible. Consider planting apple, cherry and orange trees outside. Learn about wild, local edible plants. Dehydrate as much food as possible. You should also get a smoker to use on the surface to preserve meats.

If you do not know how to cook, you should learn how to do so, as you will not be able to go out to restaurants. I have a good recipe book with over 200 recipes, for sale on my website.

Basal Metabolic Rate (BMR); the number of calories one would burn if one stayed in bed all day.

Woman	1,250
Man	1,750

The following list includes approximate amount in pounds () you need to store for some foods. If you are living in the bunker before TSHTF, whenever you use something, replace it and add to the stock. Constantly rotate and add to the supplies, when possible. Have extra seasoning, condiments, salt and powdered soups for barter. The more food you have stocked, the longer you can survive and the more you have for barter. Feel free to add anything you like to this list. This list is what I am preparing and may not be exactly what you want. Remember, store what you eat and eat what you store. Do not stock anything you will not eat.

Almonds
Almond Slivers
Apple Sauce
Apples
Baked Beans
Baking Soda
Barley (50)
BBQ Sauce
Beans (100)
Bow Ties
Bread Crumbs
Brick Cheese
Brown Rice (100)
Buckwheat
Bulgur
Canned Fruit
Canned Vegetables

Canola Oil
Cashews
Cereal
Cheddar Cheese
Cherries
Cherry Pie filling
Chocolate Chips
Chocolate Spread
Coconut, Shredded
Cookies
Cooking Spray
Crackers
Craisins
Cranberries
Cranberry Sauce
Cream of Mushroom Soup
Crushed Pineapple

Dates
Deli
DH Lemon Supreme
Dried Foods
Duck Sauce
Eggs
Egg Beaters
Flour (400)
Flour, Whole Wheat (100)
Garbanzo Beans (bags)
Garbanzo Beans (cans)
Garlic
Graham Crackers
Graham Crackers Piecrust
Granola Bars
Grape Juice
Ground Beef
Ground Chicken
Harvest Blend [2]
Hazelnuts
Hemp Milk
Hemp Protein
Honey (60)
Horse Radish
Hot Chocolate
Hot Peppers
Jelly (12)
Lemons
Lemon Juice
Lemon Pie Filling
Lentils
M&M'S
Mac & Cheese
Macaroni (50)
Maple Syrup
Marinara Sauce
Marshmallows
Marshmallow Fluff
Mashed Potatoes

Matzah, (WW)
Matzah, Egg
Matzah Meal
Mayonnaise (10)
Meats
Mozzarella Cheese
MRE's
Nori
Oats (50)
Oat Meal
Oranges
Olives
Olive Oil
Onions
Pancake Mix
Parmesan Cheese
Peanut Butter Cups
Peanut Butter (5)
Peanut Sauce
Peanuts
Pecans
Pickles
Pineapple
Pineapple Juice
Pistachio
Pizza Sauce
Pop Corn
Potato Flour
Potatoes
Potato Chips
Poultry
Powdered Drinks
Powdered Milk (1000)
Quinoa
Raisins
Red Wine Vinegar
Relish
Rice Cakes
Rice Milk

Rice Vinegar
Seitan
Salad Dressings (5)
Salmon
Salt
Seasonings
Sesame Oil
Sesame Seeds
Shredded Wheat Cereal
Sloppy Joe mix
Soup Nuts
Spaghetti (50)
Spirulina
Split Peas (10)
Steak Sauce
Stick Margarine
Sweet Potatoes
Syrup
Tahini
Tartar Sauce

Tea
Tilapia
Tofu
Tomatoes (canned)
Tomato Sauce
Tomato Paste
Tub Margarine
Tuna (Chunk & White)
Umeboshi Plum
V8
Vanilla Wafers
Vinegar
Vital Gluten
Wakame
Walnuts
Whipping Cream
Whip Topping
Wine (White & Red)

ROOT CELLAR

A ROOT CELLAR IS A great way to store some perishable foods. The basics for making a root cellar are to have good ventilation, low humidity and to make it in the coldest area in the bunker. In our case, I suggest to make it in storage area 86 which will be at the back of the basement. Any foods affected by temperature or humidity would be best stored in this area.

ROCKET STOVE

A ROCKET STOVE IS A great portable, hot burning stove. There are many ways to make one, however, this is the version I like the best. I think this will give you the best results. This is a bit complicated so there is a free version on the website for you to download to make it easier for you.

ITEMS YOU WILL NEED:
1 - No. 10 Can (Standard restaurant size can).
4 - Regular soup cans (Standard 8oz cans)
Insulation material: Sand

TOOLS:
Tin snips
Hammer and nail (to punch starter holes)
Pliers
File
Gloves
Safety glasses

HOW TO DO IT:
1. Remove all labels from the cans.
2. Take one of the four soup cans (soup can #1) and trace the shape onto the side of the No. 10 can. Cut the hole slightly above the bottom of the can to make it easier to avoid dealing with the bottom lip of the can when cutting and shaping the hole.
3. Into the No. 10 can, punch a few holes into the circle to make it easier to get the tin snips in to cut the circle.
4. Cut out the circle.
5. Use a pair of needle nose pliers to bend the edges of the hole back to get the final shape.
6. You are going to need to have a hole cut at the same height in soup can #1 so that a later soup can (soup can #2) will go through the No. 10 can and directly into soup can #1 to form an elbow.
7. To do this, place the first soup can **into** the No.10 can and place it next to the hole you cut in the No. 10 can. Take a marker and trace the hole that is already cut in the No. 10 can onto the soup can #1.
8. Make sure you have fitted a can through the No. 10 can hole to make sure it fits through cleanly but somewhat snug. You do not want any big gaps, but you also do not want to trace a hole onto the soup

can that is too small to fit the next soup can you will be inserting into it.

9. Pull the soup can out of the No. 10 can and cut out the shape drawn on it

10. Cut the shape and then round the edges back a bit for a snug fit.

11. Take your second soup can and remove the bottom. You can do this with a can opener or just use tin snips.

12. This (soup can #2) will be the horizontal burn chamber of the rocket stove.

13. You will want to "dry fit" the first two soup cans together to make sure they will fit once you assemble them inside the No.10 can. Once they fit well you can assemble these two cans inside the No. 10 can.

14. Soup can #1 with the hole cut into it should be placed into the center of the No. 10 can with the hole in the soup can lining up with the hole in the No. 10 can. The open end of soup can #1 should be facing **up** so you can insert soup can #3 into it as the chimney in a later step.

15. Soup can #2 should go through the hole in the No. 10 can and into the hole in soup can #1 to form an elbow.

16. Take your third soup can (soup can #3) and remove the top and bottom and then slit it vertically from top to bottom. You will fit this as the chimney stack, inserting it into soup can #1 that is sitting inside the No. 10 can.

17. Slice off about a quarter of an inch worth of excess can in order to crimp it down small enough to neatly fit inside of soup can #1.

18. I also recommend cutting a small arch into this can where it intersects soup can #2 coming in from the side. Otherwise the chimney will be too tall when finished. The top needs to be about a quarter inch below the top of the rim of the No. 10 can for proper use.

WWW.DOOMSDAYBUNKERBOOK.COM

19. Fit the chimney properly
20. Take the chimney (soup can #3) and trace its shape onto the lid of the No. 10 can. I am assuming the lid has already been removed. You will want to cut it out so the chimney can poke through the top of the "stove".
21. To punch the starter hole however, it is a good idea to place the lid on a piece of wood to give the nail something into which to drive. Doing so on a hard surface (a piece of wood) does not allow the nail to penetrate and doing so on dirt will bend the lid.
22. Snip the hole to size and test fit the chimney.
23. With all of the parts for the stove cut and fitted, you will want to assemble the burn chamber (soup can #1) and the elbow (soup can #2) and chimney (soup can #3) inside the No. 10 can.
24. Once assembled, you will want to fill the space left over with sand.
25. Fill the area somewhat slowly, taking time to tap the can so the sand settles into the crevices around the soup cans. Not too much though as you do not want to jar apart the assembly. Just a gentle rapping on the outside of the No. 10 should work.
26. Fill the No. 10 can to about one half inch below the rim.
27. You will want to use your tin snips to cut vertical slits in the No. 10 can from the top rim down about one half inch. This will create tabs you can then fold down to hold the lid in place. I recommend you cut eight slits so you will have four tabs that fold down and four that stay upright. The four that fold down, hold the lid down and the four that are upright will hold the cooking vessel above the flame.
28. Once the can is filled with sand, place the lid on top and fold down some of the tabs.
29. You want it so the chimney sticks up above the lid about a quarter of an inch. That leaves a gap between the opening of the chimney and the top of the No. 10 can tabs.

30. With the final soup can (soup can #4) you will want to make a small fuel shelf that will fit into the mouth of your stove. This is what the wood will rest on and at the same time allow air to travel into the stove from the bottom.
31. You want to cut a "T" shape that is roughly the same width as soup can #1 with a little wider portion at the top to keep it from sliding all the way inside the stove.
32. Cut the can to size and slip it into the mouth of the stove. You should have a large gap above the shelf and a small gap below the shelf. Without the gap at the bottom the rocket stove will not work. This lower gap is to allow oxygen into the stove.
33. While at first the stove is cool enough to hold in your hand, the outside will heat up and should not be touched with your bare hands. You will be severely burned.
34. To get the stove going use some wadded up regular paper shoved into the **chimney** with a piece of wood and light it on fire.
35. The whole reason this system works is due to the thermal differences between the chimney (HOT) and the fuel shelf (COOL).
36. Getting the whole chimney nice and hot makes it work right away. Once the fuel in the chimney burns down low enough then the fuel from the side is all that is needed to maintain a very hot flame.
37. It burns with little smoke (once lit and burning) and uses very little fuel.

ZEER FRIDGE

A ZEER FRIDGE IS A small refrigerator you can make for just a few dollars and does not require electricity. You really have to try this!

Purchase the largest (pottery) flower pot you can find. Purchase a second one that is about an inch and a half smaller than the first. Make sure the flower pots do not have holes in the bottoms. Purchase some sand. Place some sand on the bottom of the larger flower pot (about an inch of sand should do fine) to ensure the tops of the flower pots are even. Place the second flower pot inside the first one. Completely fill the space between the flower pots with the sand. Saturate the sand with as much water as possible. Put your food items in the flower pot and cover with a towel. That is all it takes. I suggest keeping this in your root cellar in storage area 83.

HENS FOR EGGS

IT would be a good idea to get a few hens to be able to have fresh eggs to eat, and for barter. If you are thinking about getting some hens, you may be wondering how many eggs they will give you every day. How many hens should you get? How do you care for them? What do you feed hens? These are good questions, and the truth is, it varies! I think there are many misconceptions about laying hens.

How many eggs you get from each hen every day depends on several factors:

- The time of year
- The breed of the hen
- The age of the hen
- Whether or not you have lighting in your chicken coop
- If your hen is molting (Hens will molt at the end of the summer or beginning of fall. This is where they lose their feathers and grow a new set.) Hens can molt for six to eight weeks.
- If your hen feels stressed because of predators, mites, or a lack of appropriate food or water

- How "free range" they are (They may lay eggs you cannot find)

If you have young hens (between six months and two years), it is bright outside, and your hens are living a relatively stress-free life, you should expect about two eggs per day from a coop of three hens. Take the number of hens you plan to purchase and multiply them by 0.75, and you will come up with the average number of eggs you will get per day.

> **Example**:
> 2 hens should give you 1 to 2 eggs per day
> 3 hens should give you 2 eggs per day
> 4 hens should give you 3 eggs per day
> 5 hens should give you 3 to 4 eggs per day
> 6 hens should give you 4 to 5 eggs per day
> 7 hens should give you 5 eggs per day
> 8 hens should give you 6 eggs per day
> 9 hens should give you 6 to 7 eggs per day
> 10 hens should give you 7 to 8 eggs per day
> 11 hens should give you 8 eggs per day
> 12 hens should give you 9 eggs per day

Hens can lay eggs into their teens, although they sometimes stop earlier. Most hens will start to lay around four to six months of age. However, for various reasons (time of year, temperature, etc.) they may wait until the next spring to start laying eggs.

The following hens are very good for producing eggs: Leghorns, Rhode Island Reds, Australorps and Orpingtons. All of these are kosher birds.

All this being said, how many hens you want will be dictated by how many eggs you want to have per day or per week.

HOUSING

THE FOLLOWING IS SOME INFORMATION you will need to know in order to care for your hens. You will need to set up some housing for them.

You will want your hens to be free range so they will be happy and produce more eggs. You will need indoor and outdoor housing for your hens.

Pine shavings cost between $6.00 - $9.00 per fifty pound bag. These may be purchased at a pet store or garden supply store.

INSIDE	• Your coup should have two square feet per bird inside. (Not including the nesting box) • Put pine wood shavings (not chips) on the floor of the coup about two inches deep • Make sure it is draft free • Keep protected from predators • Depending on where you live, you will need some heating and ventilation for the hens • For the winter, have a heat lamp • Hens do not have a problem with cold, but with draft.
NESTING BOX	• A nesting box needs to be dry, clean and relatively dark • A nesting box should be one cubic foot in size, or a bit larger • One nesting box for every two hens • Nesting material should be wood shavings, preferably pine. • The box should have a lip on it to prevent the hen from pushing out the eggs and bedding material • A box should preferably have a bar in front as a perch for the hen onto which to hop • The top should be sloped so the hen cannot sleep on the top

OUTSIDE	• You will want to have fencing that is six to seven feet tall. Start the fencing about a foot below ground to prevent predators from tunneling inside. • On top of the fencing surrounding their area, put a lightweight covering to protect the hens from overhead predators. This netting will also keep the hens from escaping. • For the top, purchase some deer netting from a local hardware store • http://www.homedepot.com/p/Deer-X-7-ft-x-100-ft-Dalen-Products-Black-Polypropylene-Protective-Fencing-DX-7/202871745 • You should figure on about ten square feet per bird of outdoor space to give them plenty of free space. • Hens love to take dust baths. They dig a shallow hole, loosen up the dirt, and proceed to get themselves absolutely as dirty as they possibly can. (Do not worry, they shake the dirt off later.) Dust baths are absolutely necessary: They prevent parasites such as mites and lice from finding a home in your chickens' feathers and legs.

FEED

I MAY BE WRONG, BUT I imagine you also want to feed your hens. I think it would be a good idea to know what they eat.

The feeders and water containers should be suspended above the ground so the birds will not contaminate the food and water with their feces.

Put them on starter ration (about two ounces) until they are eight weeks old, grower ration, or combination starter-grower, until they are eighteen weeks old, then layer ration; (about three ounces).

It is a good idea to supplement the layer ration with ground oyster shell. Oyster shell helps keep eggshells thick.

Chickens enjoy many types of food: Cooked spaghetti, clean vegetable peels, fruit, cereal, meal worms, bugs, and snails. Avoid strong tasting foods like onions and garlic; Some sources say this makes their eggs taste funny.

Scratch is a good treat for chickens. Scratch is a cracked corn and wheat mix for chickens. It is available at most feed stores. Hens love scratch.

Young chicks can be fed raw oatmeal as long as there is sufficient grit added to their diet. Without grit, chicks will be unable to obtain the nutritive value of the oatmeal.

Have fresh water available for the hens.

Do NOT give hens avocado! Avocado is poisonous to all birds. Make sure the scraps you give them are not high in sugars or fats.

Feed should cost about twenty dollars per fifty pound bag depending on your location and the variety chosen.

GENERAL CARE

CARING FOR HENS IS FAIRLY easy.

DAILY	• Keep feeders and water bowls full. • Make sure the water is clean. Chickens will be less inclined to drink dirty water, and a dehydrated bird can very quickly become ill or die. • During the winter, make sure the water is not frozen. • Check to make sure they look active, bright and healthy. • Collect and refrigerate eggs, pointy side down for maximum freshness. • If you have opened the coop door to let your hens out during the day, always be sure to close and secure it at dusk to make sure predators cannot get in. • You may leave your hens alone for a few days provided they have enough food, water and space for the duration of your trip. The eggs they will have laid in your absence will still be good to eat. Fresh eggs keep for about a week without refrigeration. • Always wash your hands before and after dealing with the hens • Have a special pair of shoes or boots for use when inside the pen
MONTHLY	• Change the bedding in the coop and the nest. This is necessary for sanitary purposes. Excessive ammonia buildup is dangerous to birds and can cause respiratory illness. • Remove the feces. Put the feces in the compost bin or use it as fertilizer.
BI-ANNUALY	• Twice a year you have to really scrub the coop clean. • Remove bedding, nest materials, food and water containers. • After cleaning, rinse well and let dry before replacing with fresh bedding. • Clean well the feed and water containers

DO NOT FEED	• Citrus fruits and peels (they can cause a drop in egg production) • Bones • Any large serving of meat • Meat that has gone bad • Garlic and onion • Avocado skins and pits • Raw potato skins • Long cut grass • Chocolate • Morning Glories • Daffodils
HANDLING	• Handing chickens is an art, and requires practice. The key is finding the balance between being gentle and letting them know that no matter how much they wriggle or squirm, they are not getting away. • First, put your dominant hand on the middle of their back. If you are new to handling chickens, it is helpful to secure their wings as much as possible with your thumb and forefinger. • Your other hand will need to secure one leg between your thumb and forefinger, and the other leg between the forefinger and middle finger of the same hand. • Then lift them, supporting the lower portion of their body with the heel of your hand and wrist. Your dominant hand should still be on their back. • Once you have them up, holding them close to your body will prevent further wriggling. • As you get better at this you will not need a hand on their backs.

WINTER	• If you have cold winters, you will not have any problems with the breeds I have mentioned. • It is not a good idea to heat the coop during the winter. Chickens adapt to the cold weather over time. Their body metabolism actually changes along with the seasons. At most, have a warming lamp. • Make sure the water supply does not freeze. If you do not have electricity in your coop and therefore cannot provide a water heater, I recommend you bring the water container inside every night, and return it outside every morning. Check the water once or twice a day to make sure it is not frozen.
SUMMER	• Excessive heat is a serious risk to birds. Make sure they have access to fresh, clean water at all times. • Provide them a source of shade outside and as much ventilation inside as possible. • Note: Your hens may lay fewer eggs during heat waves. This is a sign of stress, but laying rates will return to normal once the heat has receded.
ILLNESS	**The Following Symptoms Indicate Illness:** • Mangy appearance • Visible mites • Abnormal stool • Blood in stool • Visible worms in stool • Diarrhea • Droppings that are all white. (Normal stool is brown with a white cap.) • Sneezing • Loss of energy or depression • Sudden, drastic reduction in position in pecking order • Loss of appetite • Stunted growth

A Few Things NOT To Worry About:

- Your hen's first eggs will be pretty pathetic. They will be small, shells will be weak and some will not even have shells.
- Your hens will lose and re-grow their feathers once a year. This is called "molting" and is perfectly normal. They will not lay eggs during this time.
- A tiny speck of blood in an egg. This is normal. If it becomes frequent, or if there is a significant amount of blood, it is another story.

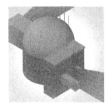

GOATS FOR MILK

HAVING a source for fresh milk is a fantastic treat for someone who is living off the grid or when TSHTF. Aside from drinking the milk yourself, it is great for barter. For Jews: If you keep *cholav Yisrael*, you cannot get more *cholav Yisrael* than milking your own goat.

An average doe can supply about three quarts of milk a day. That is much more than you will probably need. You can use the excess to make cheese, yogurt and ice cream. Goat milk has a reputation of having a bad taste. The problem is this reputation is not earned. Goat milk may have a bad taste if there was a buck present at milking time; his presence can sour the milk.

More people consume goat milk than cow milk. Goats are hardy animals: They adapt well to heat and cold, productively forage and graze, require little space, and are inexpensive to keep. Since mature does (females) usually weigh between 120 and 135 pounds, they are much easier to handle than cows, which can weigh 1,000 pounds each. Goats may surprise you in other ways, as well. They are highly intelligent and remarkably friendly creatures. Since they are active, extremely agile and very curious, their antics may amuse you for hours. With all this in mind, it is easy to see why dairy goats can be the ideal addition to your setup.

It is best to purchase two does at the same time so they will not be lonely. Does are herd animals and do not like to be alone. Alone, she will be very loud and get into mischief.

Alpines, Oberhaslis, Saanens, and Toggenburgs are four popular breeds for milking that are good for cooler climates as they themselves come from the Swiss Mountains. You can expect to pay anywhere from $75 to $500 for a goat.

HOUSING

YOU WILL NEED A SIMPLE shelter for your goats. Your shelter should have about fifteen square feet or more, for each goat. It should be clean, dry and draft free, but well ventilated. Make sure the goats cannot climb onto the roof of their shelter.

Stalls should be equipped with a rack for hay, a trough or box for grain, and a water pail holder. Include extra space for storing feed and other supplies, as well as a stand for milking. Separate the storage and milking areas from the goat quarters with a wall or partition four feet high. It is important to keep the bedding clean and dry. Top off the bedding as needed with fresh straw and replace bedding that gets damp or soiled. Remember: Goat manure and bedding are great for the garden.

The floor of the shelter should have a thick covering of wood shavings, straw or hay.

OUTSIDE

GIVE YOUR GOATS PLENTY OF outside space where they can play, exercise and forage to their hearts' content. It is suggested that you have a minimum of 200 square feet per goat.

You will need a good, sturdy fence at least five feet high. From what I have learned, a good chain link fence would be sufficient. Goats are notorious escape artists, as they can climb trees, jump over fences, chew through rope and wriggle their way through the smallest of spaces. Therefore, it is essential you erect a strong, goat-proof fence around the pen. You need to lock the fence of the pen as goats can open gates.

FOOD

IT IS BEST TO ALLOW your goats access to pasture and forage. They will eat whatever is available. Goats are opportunistic feeders and appreciate a varied diet. This characteristic not only saves you time and labor, but helps reduce your feeding costs. Try to keep an eye on what is growing in their pasture. Some types of plants, such as wild onions, can drastically alter the flavor of the milk. Make sure your goats have some type of roughage year-round, such as twigs, bark or leaves. Corn and sunflower stalks from the garden are another good source, as well as a fine-stemmed hay, such as alfalfa or clover.

In addition to pasture and/or forage, a milking doe should receive two to three pounds of commercial feed each day, such as a sixteen percent dairy ration, along with three or more pounds of hay. The amount will vary depending on other food sources, quality of feed and your goat. Ask your breeder about their feeding program. Provide fresh water at all times.

Goat-proof any areas that might have plants growing that can be toxic to goats, such as oleander, yew and larkspur.

For treats, you may give them a wide selection of fruits and vegetables, including apples, pears, peaches, watermelon, banana, carrots, celery, squash and spinach. Just avoid giving them potatoes, tomatoes and kale, as these can be poisonous to goats.

BREEDING

WHEN YOUR DOES REACH MATURITY - which happens when they are six to eight months or weigh at least eighty pounds, they are ready for breeding. Their yearly heat cycles usually begin around August or September. Does remain in heat for three days, usually on a seventeen to twenty-one day cycle. Put your does and buck together at this time.

If you do not own a buck, you can either hire a buck or bring your does to a farm that has a buck. You will have to pay a stud fee, which is usually somewhere between fifty to one-hundred dollars.

Once you have a buck of your own, you can recoup the stud fee by hiring out your buck to others and for your own does.

It can be difficult to tell if a doe is pregnant, so one of the best signs of a successful mating is a milky-white colored discharge coming from her genital area.

A goat's pregnancy lasts about 150 days, or five months and most pregnancies will produce two kids.

Young does are usually easy to deal with, as the demand for milk-producing does is high and you can sell them to other goat owners as soon as they are weaned. If you like, you can keep the female offspring of your best milking doe, as she can take her mother's place in a couple of years.

Bucks are a bit more difficult. The majority of young bucks should be castrated by the time they are three weeks of age, as they will ultimately be sold for meat. You can do this as soon as they are weaned, or wait until they have reached maturity. I suggest you keep one buck as a breeding sire. However, keep the buck separate from the does.

MILKING

KEEP THE MILK SUPPLY FLOWING by breeding your does once a year.

The doe will start to give milk after the kids are born.

During the milking period, you and the kids can share the milk; the doe should provide plenty. The best plan is after the kids are two weeks old to confine them overnight and milk the doe in the morning. After her morning milking, leave the kids with the doe to nurse at will.

Milking is easy to learn: Ask anyone who has ever milked a cow or goat to show you. Milking is easier if you feed the does grain as you milk them. Milk out both udders completely and milk at about the same time each day. Keep your milking equipment and area clean. Once you have finished milking, cool the milk-filled container as quickly as possible by setting it into a large pan filled with cold water for about fifteen minutes. Occasionally stirring the milk with a clean utensil will help it cool evenly. Once the milk has cooled, pour it into glass containers and refrigerate immediately.

Goat milk differs from cow milk in that the butterfat globules are smaller, so they disperse easily, making goat milk naturally homogenized. Unlike cow milk, the cream will not separate on its own, so goat milk products will be much smoother and creamier. If you want to make butter, you will need a cream separator. Another difference you may notice is goat milk appears whiter than cow milk.

Once a doe has produced her first offspring, she will start producing milk and will continue to do so for approximately 305 days following delivery.

The milk flow is usually highest two to three months after giving birth then tapers off towards the end of the lactation cycle. The doe will require a two month "dry spell" before she gives birth a second time and begins producing milk again. In the dairy world, this is known as "freshening".

If you have never milked an animal before, it is important to get the technique right. Rather than tugging on the teat, you need to wrap your hand around it, cutting off the milk supply at the top using your thumb and forefinger. Then you can use your other fingers to squeeze the teat and extract the milk.

At first, you might find milking to be somewhat slow and awkward, and it could take you up to half an hour per goat. However, after a while, you will be a pro and be able to do it much faster.

ILLNESS

SOME OF THE MOST COMMON and visible symptoms of a sick goat are: Not eating or drinking, crusty eyes, diarrhea, hot udders, pressing its face against a wall or fence, coughing, crying or calling more than usual, grinding teeth, separating itself from the group, pale eyelids and gray gums.

Your goats will also need yearly vaccinations against tetanus and enterotoxemia (an overeating disease) and you will need to watch out for parasites like lice and ticks.

CARE

GENERALLY, GOATS DO NOT REQUIRE much grooming. However, you will need to give them some attention every now and then in order to keep them clean and comfortable.

BRUSHING	Goats should be brushed at least once a year (preferably at the start of summer when they are shedding) with a firm-bristled grooming brush. This removes dandruff and loose hair, stimulates blood flow, and gives you a chance to check for any lumps on the skin or other signs of diseases.
BATHING	Bathing your goats is not required, but it helps to remove lice and makes clipping easier.
CLIPPING	Clip your goats hair at least once a year, to help them stay cool throughout the summer. You may want to clip the tail and udder regions of female goats more frequently, to help keep them clean during milking and kidding season.
HOOVES	Trim your goats' hooves about once a month, otherwise they will become overgrown and difficult to walk on. This is a relatively quick and easy process, which you can do with a pocket or roofing knife.

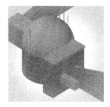

HONEYBEES

RAISING bees for honey is a phenomenal idea of which I have heard others talking. Personally, I am not going to be doing this since I am highly allergic to bees. Having fresh raw honey is also a fantastic barter item.

If this is going to be your first time working with honeybees, I strongly suggest you go to a bee farm a few times and watch and learn some of the secrets and tricks for dealing with honeybees. More importantly, you will learn how to **act** around bees. It would also be a good idea to have someone with you the first couple of times you are working with your own bee colony.

There are many ways to raise honeybees. Some people use old logs or boxes. However, although it is more expensive, it is much more productive, and safe, to use a commercial beehive kit. A complete kit from a bee supply company should include all the hive parts, a smoker, hive tool, gloves, hat and veil. The whole kit should cost about one-hundred dollars. However, you will still need the bees.

There are several options for acquiring bees. The best and easiest is to find them online and have them shipped to you. For about thirty dollars, you can probably get about 10,000 working bees and a queen bee.

Once you receive your bees, you will put the queen bee into your hive and then pour in your worker bees. This is perfectly safe as they are still tired from the trip and they have no hive to defend.

The first job the worker bees will be doing is setting up their new home. They will spend their time building up their numbers to about 100,000 to maintain their hive and produce the honey. They will also be working to store up supplies for the winter. This means that you will not be able to harvest any honey until the next season.

WORKER BEES

BEES BASICALLY TAKE CARE OF themselves. You do not have to feed or water them. You do not have to clean up after them.

Worker bees are unfertile female bees. They run the hive, feed and clean the queen, gather nectar, pollen and water. They will also maintain the temperature in the hive. The workers also feed the larvae and make beeswax.

Worker bees usually live only about six weeks and will have gathered enough nectar to make 1/12 a teaspoon of honey.

The males are drones and do not work at all.

1. Visit the bees on a sunny day when nectar-bearing plants are in bloom. Most of the bees will be out working the flowers - and the rest will be too busy to worry about you.
2. Wear white or light-colored clothing. Do not wear wool. Tuck your shirt into your pants and your pant legs into your socks. Wear a hat, bee veil and gloves.

3. Do not wear perfume.
4. Make sure you do not smell from your hens or goats.
5. Wash your beekeeping outfit regularly, especially after you were stung. If you do not, the residual odor of any past bee stings will act as an attack alarm, and every time you visit, you will get stung more.
6. Use a bellows smoker.
7. Get some of the smoke on yourself

I am not going into detail how to check on your queen to make sure she is doing her job. Since I cannot do this myself, I cannot do first hand research as I have done on the other sections. You will need to learn how to take care of your queen and the hive to be able to get a good harvest. Also, the care of the queen and checking on the hive will be dependent on the specific type of hive that you purchase or use.

BEE STINGS

IF YOU DO GET STUNG:

1. Do not jerk your hand back and drop the frame you are holding. That is asking for more trouble.
2. Promptly scrape the stinger out with your fingernail or hive tool, and you will get so little poison you may not swell a bit. If you try to grab it, you will squeeze more venom into your system.
3. Smoke the spot. A stinging bee releases a banana-scented pheromone to alert its comrades to attack the same area.

LOCATION

YOU WANT TO HAVE YOUR honeybees in a good location. Ideally, you want them to have sun in the morning and be in shade in the afternoon. This will get them active in the morning to do their work and they will not have to expend as much energy cooling the hive. This way they will spend more energy making honey.

Make sure you do not have them on top of a hill or a very windy area. You may want to put them in a location where you can watch them. I have not incorporated a hive location in any of my drawings because the hive should be located outside of the compound.

HARVESTING

IT IS FAIRLY EASY TO get the honey. First, remove the frames from the hive and then brush the bees off the frame.

There are basically two ways to remove the honey from the frame.

The simple way to harvest, is to take a pocket knife and cut out honeycomb chunks.

The better way is to cut the caps off all the sealed cells and spin the liquid honey out in a centrifuge called a "honey extractor". The advantage of the centrifuge is you will get higher yields, but the centrifuge costs about $200.

I have heard of beekeepers getting from fifty to one-hundred pounds of honey from each hive.

SEASONINGS & CONDIMENTS

ONE of the most difficult things about living in a bunker or during a crisis, is having access to good food. If you have access to a good amount of condiments and seasonings, you will not get bored of the food. In a SHTF situation, this will also come in handy, and seasonings and condiments will be great for barter; especially salt. Keep in storage areas 59, 95, 98.

10X Sugar	Curry
All Spice	Dill
Almond Extract	Fennel
Bakers Chocolate	Food Coloring
Baking Powder	Garlic Powder
Baking Soda	Garlic Salt
Basil	Ginger
Beef Soup Powder	Hungarian Paprika
Brown Sugar	Italian Seasonings
Cardamom	Ketchup
Chicken Soup Powder	Kosher Salt
Cinnamon	Minced Onions
Cloves	Mrs. Dash
Coriander	Mushroom Soup Powder
Corn Syrup	Mustard
Cumin	Nutmeg

Old Bay
Onion Powder
Onion Salt
Onion Soup Powder
Oregano
Paprika
Parsley Flakes
Pepper
Pop Corn Salt
Poppy Seed
Red Wine
Relish
Rosemary
Saffron

Salt
Season/Rub
Season Salt
Sesame Seed
Shortening
Soy Sauce
Sugar
Sumac
Tamari
Vanilla Extract
White Wine
Yeast

KITCHEN SUPPLIES

KITCHEN appliances and supplies will be kept in storage areas 60 and 99. You should have duplicates as some items are delicate and may break after extensive use.

Aluminum Foil	Cutting Boards
Bamboo Mat (for Sushi)	Deep Fryer
Baster	Dehydrator
Blender	Dishes
Boning Knife	Egg Brush
Bottle Opener	Egg Separator
Bowls	Egg Slicer
Bread Maker	Fillet Knife
Burger Press	Food Processor
Buss Buckets	Forks
Can Opener	Frying Pans
Casserole Dishes	Funnel
Cheese Cloth	Glasses
Chopper	Grater
Coffee Filters	Griddle
Colander	Grill
Cookie Sheets	Grinder
Crinkle Cutter	Jar Opener
Crock-pot	Knives

Ladles
Measuring Cups
Measuring Spoons
Meat Fryer
Mixer
Mixing Bowls
Mugs
O2 Absorbers
Pans
Parchment Paper
Peeler
Plates
Pots
Potato Masher
Pressure Cooker
Roasting Pan
Rotisserie
Saran Wrap
Scale

Scaling Knife
Scraper
Scrub Buds (steel wool)
Serving Utensils
Spatula
Sponges
Spoon Rests
Spoons
Steel
Stock Pot
Strainers
Tenderizer
Trash Bags
Vacuum Packer
Wax Paper
Whisk
Wood Spoons
Zip Lock Bags

Kitchen counters in the bunker should be 30 inches deep, as well as all kitchen cabinets. This means storage areas 59 and 60.

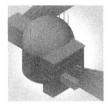

INVENTORY

THE following is a compilation of what I suggest you keep in the bunker. Please take my list and modify it for your own needs. This list does not include the bug-out kits listed further. There are items not specifically on this list, mentioned elsewhere. A number of items on this list may be mentioned elsewhere in this book. However, the reason for mentioning them here is to indicate where they are going to be stored and a quantity.

Walk around your current house or apartment and take note of what you have. You want to have some creature comforts and be able to live well.

For a more complete list with more information, download it free at the website, www.doomsdaybunkerbook.com.

AO = All Over   OF = Office
AR = Area   SH = Shed
DR = Dining Room   OU = Outside
LR = Living Room   * = Backup, Not Essential

ITEM	#	INFO	AR
2"X4" Lumber	10		82 *
4X8 3/4"	3		82 *

Plywood			
5 Gallon Bucket	5+	Plus lids - For water reuse, etc $4@	80
55 Gallon Barrel	21	For water	AO
Airwave	1	Sprint (repeater for cell phone)	50
Alcohol	5		19
Ammo Boxes	5	http://www.amazon.com/MTM-Forest-Green-Caliber-Storage/dp/B003TNV46O/ref=br_lf_m_1001140791_1_10_img/186-0298701-9219901?_encoding=UTF8&s=sporting-goods&pf_rd_m=ATVPDKIKX0DER&pf_rd_s=center-3&pf_rd_r=01ZM6W4225STWHM8HZAV&pf_rd_t=1401&pf_rd_p=1635249502&pf_rd_i=1001140791	104
Ammo		Several boxes of different types for barter	104 *
Archery Kit		For self defense	56
Batteries		9, AA, AAA, C & D (Rechargeable)	20 *
Battery Charger	2		20
Bed	1		10
Blanket	2		22 *
Bleach	4		66
Books			15,26,27,28
Boots			46
Borax	2		18
Bricks	10		82 *
Broom	1	& Dustpan	56
Bubble Wrap			82
Bug Spray	5		41

Cameras	2		50
Candles	30	3-4 day candles	20 *
Car Batteries	4	For booby-traps on ramps & NBC Filter	
Car Port	1	To hide the van	OU
Carpet		Pieces around the bunker	AO
C Crane Radio	1	Emergency radio	50 *
Ceiling Fan	2	Above the DR table & in the bedroom	DR BR
Charcoal Briquettes	2		84 *
Chicken Wire			OU
Cinder Blocks	10		82 *
Cinder Slabs	10		82 *
Clock	2		14,50
Clothes			1,2,3,4,6,7,8
Crayon Boxes	3	Can be used for candles, melt and sealer	18 *
Cube Crates		As many as possible	AO
Curtain	1	For toilet area	64
Curtain Rod	1		64
Deer Net			OU
Dishes			60
Dish Soap	10		99
Disposable Cutlery		1 case each, forks, knives, spoons, soup spoons	99
Disposable Dishes		1 case each, plates, bowls	99
Dog Food	60	900# per dog per year (15# bag)	106
Dog Mats			105
Door Alarm	2	One for each hatch	
Door Barricade	5	http://www.rakuten.com/prod/masterlock-security-bar-265dccsen/204290650.html	AO

Door Sweep	5	For insulation	
Drop Cloth	2	For protection	103 *
Drying Rack	2	For clothes	66
Duct Tape	1	Case 50 yards 2.8" 8 rolls	103 *
Electric Photo Sensor	5		103*
Electric Wire	1		44
Electromagneti c Lock	2	One for each hatch	
Emergency Blanket	2		22 *
Entertainment		Stereo, TV, Dish, VCR	50
Environmental Suits	2		46 *
Expanding Foam	5	Cans	103
Extension Cord	5	50' @ and some smaller ones	44
	7		
Exterior Doors	7	Locks for doors	
	21	Hinges for doors	
Fans for Venting	2	http://www.homedepot.com/p/Air-King-Advantage-50-CFM-Ceiling-Exhaust-Fan-AS50/203258495?N=5yc1vZc4kqZ1z0umskZ1z0yi0z#specifications	BR
Faraday Cage	4	Make your own	
File Cabinet	2	4 drawer each	70
Firearms			AO
Fire Extinguisher	5	Make sure they are ABC. Put these on each level and outside	AO
Fire Starters			20
Flare Gun	2	Plus spare flares	AO
Flashlight		Powerful ones on all levels	20
Flex Seal	4	www.getflexseal.com	103

Floss	10		66
Flower Pots	10	12"	LR
Foam Pad	8	For hatches, doors and dog beds - Full size	AO
Folding Chairs	2		70
Freezer	1	20.7 CF	123
Game Box	1	Chess, checkers, etc	50
Gas Mask	2	http://www.amazon.com/gp/product/B004NJS7VS/ref=as_li_ss_tl?ie=UTF8&tag=yt0c-20&linkCode=as2&camp=1789&creative=390957&creativeASIN=B004NJS7VS	46 *
Gasoline	100		84 *
Garden Hose	2	50' XHose Pro	54
Garden Tools			OU
Generator	1		SH*
Grounding Rod	1		OU
Hand Lotion	4		66
Hand Soap	2		66
Hand Truck	1		72
Hand Warmers	1	Case	19 *
Hatch	2	http://www.americanbombshelter.com/flat-blast-hatch.html (24x38)	
Hay		Timothy for hens and & goats	OU
Hot Plates	3		115
IBC	6	Size of IBC 48"L x 40"W x 54"H	LR
Jet Pump	1	For the well	37
Keyboard	1	Some musical instrument	DR
Kitchen Sink	1		
Ladder	1		72
Lanterns			20 *
Laptop	2		OF
Laundry Soap	2		66
Light Bulbs	14	LED	103
Light Fixtures	16		AO

Light Sticks	1	Case of 25 6"	20 *
Lighter Fluid	5		85 *
Linen	2	Have extra for emergency supplies	22
Litter			65, 105
Mason Jars		For a set of 12, 8 oz	99
Matches			20
Medical Kit	1		19
Microwave	1		58
Mirror	1	Full length on inside of the door of the bedroom hall	
Mop	1		56
Motor Oil			84
Mouthwash	4		66
Napkins	1	Case	101
NBC Filtration System		http://www.americanbombshelter.com/60-CFM-ACDC-Safe-Cell-complete-system.html	61
NBC Filters	1	ASR-100-FIL replacement filter set	61
Night Lights	8		103
NIOSH N95	1	Dust masks	46
Office Books			53
Pad Lock	1	And chain for generator	SH
Pans			60
Paper	3	Cases	100
Paper Shades	2	For shed (for pack of 4)	SH
Paper Towels	2	Cases	101
Paracord	2		103*
Pepper Spray	2		AO
Petroleum Jelly	2		18
Plant Nutrients		Ph tester	48
Plant Seeds			48
Playing Cards	1		50
Pellets	10+	For fireplace 40# bags $20.00	81
Pellet Stove	1		49

Pet First Aid Kit			19
Pool Table	1	OK, this is for me	LR
Pots			60
Pressurized Water Tank	1	http://www.homedepot.com/p/Fl otec-85-Gal-Pre-Charged-Pressure-Tank-with-220-Gal-Equivalent-Rating-FP7130/100184364	37
Printer	2		53
Propane Grill	1	For backup	96*
Propane Heater	1	For backup	96*
Propane, Large	16	34# no-exchange ($50)/34# exchange ($20)	85
Propane, Small	24	16.4# ($3)	85
Propane Stove	1	For backup	96*
Protection		Weapons, knives, stun gun, flare gun, pepper spray, etc	AO
Pup Tent	1		96 *
Radon Fan	1	If needed	33
Radon Test Kit	2		18
Rags			101
Refrigerator	1	30 CF	58
Refrigerator	2	Small (in shed & storage)	*SH
Rope	2	Nylon	103 *
Router	1		53
Rubber Gloves	5	Boxes	99
Safe	1		124
Salt		For snow	46
Sand	2	$20 per cubic yard	105 *
Saran Wrap	2		99
Sawdust			105
Sewing Kit			18
Shampoo	2		66

Shed	1	12X24 or larger	OU
Shoe Rack	2	Hanging on the bedroom hall door	BR
Shovel	1	Dirt	60
Shower Kit	1	Freesia-38-in-x-38-in-x-78-in-Shower-Kit-in-White	LR
Snow Shovel	1		41
Sofa	2		LR
Software			O
Steel Wool	2		99
Step Ladder	1		72
Sterno Fuel	2	Case of 12 cans	84 *
Stove	1	http://products.geappliances.com/ApplProducts/Dispatcher?REQUEST=SpecPage&Sku=JGB650DEFBB	58
Stun Gun	2		5,54
Suitcases	2		96
Sump Pump	1		46
Surveillance System	1	http://www.amazon.com/DEFENDER-21031-SENTINEL-8-Channel-Resolution/dp/B007ULT4K4/ref=lp_898406_1_11?s=photo&ie=UTF8&qid=1400466539&sr=1-11	OF
Tank-less Water Heater	1	http://www.homedepot.com/p/Eemax-Single-Point-2-4-kW-120-Volt-Electric-Tankless-Water-Heater-SP2412/203985266?N=5yc1vZc1tyZ2bcoqqZ1z0uhtu	58
Tarp	4	2 for use in bunker, 2 for backup	103
Tissue	24		101
Toaster Oven	1		100
Toilet Paper	50	Rolls or more per person	65
Toner			100
Tooth Brush	4		66
Tooth Paste	4		66

Towels			99
Trash Bags	2	Cases	99
Trash Compactor	1	Manual	67
Vitamins			19
Walkie Talkie	2		50
Wash Board	1	For washing clothing	66 *
Wash Cloths			22
Water Filter System	1	Get extra filters	65
Water Purification	2	Tablets	18 *
Waterless Soap	4		66
Weather Station	1	http://www.weathershack.com/product/la-crosse-technology-ws-2815u-it.html	48
Wood for Burning			81
Wood Stove	1		49
Zeer Pot Fridge	1		102*
Power Strips	5		97

Cinder Block (CMU) Size - 8"X8"X16" $1.30@
Cinder Slab Size - 8"X2"X16" $1.00@

SPECIFICALLY FOR JEWS

150 year Calendar
Besamim
Challah board and knife
Challah cover
Chanukah Menorah
Chumash
Eruv poles
Gemarahs

Havdalah Candle
Kidush cup
Kittel
Machzorim
Megilah
Mezuzos
Passover Dishes
Passover Food

Passover Plate, etc
Passover Pots & Pans
Sechach
Sefirah Calendar
Seforim
Shabbat Candles
Shofar

Siddur
Stender (lectern)
Succah
Talis
Tefillin

TRANSPORTATION

IN the event of having to bug-out **and** if you want to go to town, you will need some way to get around. The following is what I suggest for vehicles. Always keep your vehicle's gas tanks full. Keep at least one-hundred gallons of gas in stock at all times. Keep gas in storage area 84. Store gasoline in approved safe gasoline storage containers.

Keep all your vehicles are well maintained. Also keep extra oil, transmission oil, windshield washer fluid and any other fluids they may need, on hand. Also keep extra filters, tires, batteries, etc.

CAR

FOR REGULAR TRANSPORTATION, I SUGGEST a Chevy Suburban. This would be good for general transportation and moving. This is a very strong and rugged vehicle that would also be a good vehicle in case you need to bug-out.

RV

IN CASE OF HAVING TO bug-out (an unlikely occurrence) from the bunker, I suggest you have a second vehicle. This second vehicle should be an RV as it would also give you living space on the go. The RV should be stocked with all its fluids at all times. Get the largest RV you can afford. You can also put solar panels and a water collection system on the roof of the RV.

TRAILER

IN CASE OF HAVING TO bug-out from the bunker, have a hitch trailer attached to the Suburban to transport your food, water and other supplies. Keep two (2) - fifty-five gallon water barrels in the trailer at all times. Get the largest trailer you can afford.

GOLF CART

IN ORDER TO MAKE IT easier to get around such a large property, I suggest getting a golf cart. Get extra batteries for the golf cart and keep them charged at all times.

TOOLS

STORE tools in storage area 103. Tools like the wood splitter would need to be stored outside.

Air (cans)	Filters
Ax	Fishing Line
Bolts	Flat Head Screw Drivers
Brackets	Floss
Bungee Cords	Flower Pots
C Clamps	Funnel
Calk	Gloves
Chain Saw	Glue
Chisel	Glue Gun
Circular Saw	Hair Bands
Coffee Filters	Hammer
Colored Tape	Hand Saw
Drill	Hand Shovel
Drill Bits	Head Band Flash Light
Dryer Sheets	Hoses
Duct Tape	Knives
Electrical Tape	Level
Elmer's Glue	Lock Wrench
Extension cords	Machete
Files	Marker

Nail Polish
Nails
Needle Nose Pliers
Nuts
Oil for Generator
Packing Tape
Paint Brush
Patio Leveling Sand
Pencil
Philips Screw Drivers
Pipe Cleaners
Pipe Cutter
Pipes, PVC
Pliers
Pocket Knife Tool
Rat Trap - Spring Type
Razor Blades
Rope
Rotary Saw
Sand Paper
Sander
Screws

Shovel
Socket Wrenches
Soldering Gun
Staples
Staple Gun
Steel Wool
Tape Measure
Teflon Tape
Tool Box
Twine
Velcro
Vice Grips
Volt Meter
Washers
WD-40
Wire Cutter
Wire Nuts
Wood Splitter
Wrenches
Zip Ties

INCOME

OH no! Do we have to discuss this? Unfortunately, the answer is "Yes". Unless you are independently wealthy. If you are independently wealthy, go to the next chapter.

It would be a good idea if you can do your job remotely. If you can do your job by telecommuting, you would be more secure with being off the grid.

In my design for the bunker, I have set aside an area for your office and office supplies.

SOFTWARE

IN ORDER TO WORK FROM home, you will need several software programs. I will only mention a few of the myriad number of programs available. All of these programs are free, or have a free version. I am sure you can afford free. I am not endorsing these programs, however, I do use every one of these.

PROGRAM	FUNCTION
7Zip	File compression
Ad-Aware	Anti-malware
Adobe	File format

Acrobat	
AOL Messenger	Chat program
AVG free	Free anti-virus
DropBox	On line backup, file sharing
Evernote	Note taking, sharing, lists & more
FileZilla	File sharing and transfer
GBridge	Google program which allows remote access to other computers
Gimp	Photo editing
Google	Google Earth, email, calendar, online backup & more
MagicISO	Makes CD's and DVD's
Mozy Home	On line backup
One Drive	On line backup
Open Office	Word processor, database, drawing, math, and more
PayPal	Make and receive payments
SketchUp	Drafting
Skype	Video and chat program
Spybot	Anti-spyware
SyncBack	Backup
Team Viewer	Remote control and access of a computer
Ubuntu	Operating system
Yahoo!	Chat program, email

Depending on what you do for a living, you may want access to a fax line. Do not spend money on a fax machine and a dedicated fax line. I use an online fax service. There are many different services available and they vary with services and pricing. Do your research and you can get a good deal for about twenty-five dollars per month.

Most banks will allow you to do all your banking online without ever having to walk into the bank. There are some banks that will allow you to deposit checks into your account by just taking a photograph of it with your smart phone. Some banks even have their own apps.

HARDWARE

THIS IS NOT THE FORUM to discuss your specific needs for a computer, however, I want to suggest several general ideas. If you are able to do so, I suggest you get the latest version of whatever you buy since it may be a while until you can upgrade.

COMPUTER	Laptop with a docking station
MONITOR	Even with a laptop, get a large dual flat screen setup
BATTERY	Despite having a laptop, get a UPS for extra battery time
PRINTER	Get a good black & white and a separate color printer
HARD DRIVE	Get a three terabyte hard drive and a second one for mirroring. Get two more for backups.
TABLET	This will be helpful for a number of areas

BACKUP

ONE THING I CANNOT STRESS enough - backup your files. In the chart above, I mentioned four free services. I also mentioned a free program that will allow you to backup your files locally. Here are a few suggestions I invite you to employ. Personally, I do all of the following every day, most of which are automated. Did I mention you should regularly backup your files?

1. Do all of your work saved to an external hard drive
2. Backup that hard drive to another external hard drive - daily
3. Swap this hard drive out on a weekly basis. Store this hard drive in the safe (faraday cage).
4. Backup your main hard drive (#1 above) to the computer's internal hard drive - daily
5. Backup your files to multiple online services - daily.
6. Backup your critical files (or all of them depending on your needs) to flash drives - daily or as needed.

7. Store the flash drives in a faraday cage.
8. Mirror your operating system hard drive

I know it is a chore, but most of these tasks can be automated. Please backup your files at least on a weekly basis.

CELL PHONE TOWER

HERE IS ANOTHER IDEA FOR passive income of which you may not have thought. You could lease a part of your property to cell phone carriers. Depending on your property size and location, and their needs, the carriers may be interested in this. In fact, you may be able to get several carriers on one tower. Carriers will pay anywhere from $100 - $60,000 per year. This is great passive residual income.

HORSE

ANOTHER IDEA FOR PASSIVE RESIDUAL income is to lease part of your property as a horse farm. You do not have to do anything for the horses, the owners of the horses or the farriers will take care of the horses. You are just supplying the land, a fence and a barn.

By the way, Do not forget to backup your files.

In due time, I will have more ideas for passive income on the website.

OFFICE SUPPLIES

OFFICE supplies & equipment will be kept in storage areas 51 & 100. File cabinets in storage area 70. Extra levels of the shelves will be needed. You will want multiples of almost everything in this list.

Accordion File	Laptops
Air (can)	Lead
Batteries	Loose-leaf Binders
Binder Clips	Magnifying Light
Calculator	Markers
CD's	Masking Tape
Drawing Tablet	Mouse (External)
DVD's	Mouse Pad
Eraser	Pads of Paper
File Cabinet	Paper
File Cards	Paper Clips
File Folders	Paper Shredder
Flash Drives	Pencils
Folders	Pencil Sharpener
Hard Drive (External)	Pens
Highlighter	Post it Notes
Horizontal Files	Power Strips
Ink Refills	
Keyboard (External)	Printers

Printer Ink
Printer Paper
Rubber Bands
Ruler
Scales
Scissors
Scotch Tape
Scrap Paper
Shelf Makers
Speakers
Stapler

Staples
Tablet
Ties
Toner
Tool Box
Triangles
Twisty Ties
USB Cables
White Out

WOMEN & CHILDREN

MOST preppers, as am I, are men, so I write this chapter to men. When you are making plans for your bunker, you must take into consideration your spouse and children. There is an old expression, "Happy wife, happy life." I am going to make a few suggestions, which I hope will make bunker living more comfortable and enjoyable for your family.

Here is the challenge I am facing. By default, I am a man and therefore I am dealing with the deficit of being from the male species and trying to give advice on making your bunker more enjoyable for your wife and children. You see my conundrum?

It is the job of the husband to protect and take care of his family. As far as a woman is concerned, she may consider acquiring medical knowledge, and educating the children. It is going to be the woman who is going to help organize and take care of the children and the bunker. Make sure she has the tools she needs.

WIFE

- Your wife is your **equal** partner in this endeavor.
- In all your planning, ALWAYS consider your wife's feelings and concerns.
- Make the inside of the bunker aesthetically pleasing.
    - Put up some pictures and paintings
    - Paint the bunker
    - Do something nice with the floor
    - When furnishing the bunker, get furniture she likes.
    - Since you are going to be planting a garden both inside and outside the bunker, consider a few flowery plants for her.
- Stock foods your wife enjoys
- In most families, it is the woman who does most of the cooking. Make sure the kitchen appliances are to her liking.
- Have books and movies your wife enjoys.
- Always help your wife in the kitchen and with cleaning.
- Wash the dishes.

CHILDREN

THE IDEA OF A DOOMSDAY scenario or TEOTWAWKI is frightening enough for adults. I cannot imagine what it must be like for children. With this in mind, I will make a few suggestions for someone who is prepping with children.

- Be sure to include your children in your prepping, in a fun way.
- Include your children in your prepping plans
- Give them tasks they enjoy
- When you are including your children with your plans and prepping, make sure they **enjoy** the

process or they will be turned off and reject your plans.

- Have plenty of games and good entertainment for your children.
- Have good educational books and games for them
- Do NOT forget their education
- Consider homeschooling your children
- Make sure you stock foods for them
- Many children enjoy working with animals. You are going to have hens and goats. Gently teach them how to deal with these wonderful animals.
- I have suggested a large dog. When getting a dog, get one that is good with children and who your children like.

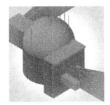

AQUAPONICS SYSTEM

I assume you will occasionally want to eat. In this chapter we will discuss how to make an aquaponics system that will allow you to grow fresh fruits and vegetables and raise edible fish. You will make an aquaponics garden that will be self-sustaining, aside from occasionally adding some fish food and checking the Ph about once a week. All fish will be edible as well as all the plants in the garden and around the bunker. The plants will help produce oxygen and clean the air.

Make sure to get duplicates of all parts of the garden. Listed below is just for the system, not the backups. Keep the backup equipment and supplies under the water tanks. Have an extra backup battery grid just for the garden - for the lights and pumps.

My idea for the aquaponics system is to have two IBC's side by side with about two feet of space between them. The extra space is for maintenance and harvesting purposes. Each IBC will be cut and rebuilt in order to make two complete gardens to house about a dozen fish each, plus many plants. Everything will be edible. Each IBC will hold approximately 300 gallons of water. There will be a water pump and an air pump in each tank.

Get duckweed as a food source for the tilapia fish. The duckweed will replicate itself. It takes about nine months for a tilapia to mature to be able to be consumed (about 1.5 - 2 pounds). Tilapia eat duckweed, ground-up salad greens, worms and algae. Keep the fish tanks as dark as possible. Consider putting a cloth around the tank to keep the tank dark.

Have a supply of worms and leeches. Learn how to grow seaweed.

The following website will give you all the information you need to be able to make the system I am making. http://ibcofaquaponics.com/

EQUIPMENT

Item	Size	Quantity	Cost	$
2X4 Lumber	8'	2	$3	$6
Air Pump (ac/dc)		2	$30	$60
Air Stone		2	$3	$6
Air Tubing				
Barbed Threaded Elbow, PVC	1"	2		
Fish		25		
Fish Food	10L	2	$83	$166
Fish Net, Large		1		$25
Fish Net, Small		1		$3
Fish Tank	600 gal	2 IBC (2)	$200	$400
Grow Bed	(1)	2 IBC (2)	0	0
Grow Lights		4+		
Grow Medium (Expanded Clay)		(400L)		
Net Breeder		1		$6
Pipe (this may be wrong size)	.656"	2"		
PVC Elbows	1"	8	$3	$24
PVC Pipe	1"	30'	$4	$12

Reducing Coupling	1.5"-1"	2		
Seeds				
Siphon		1		
Storm pipe (6")	12"	2		
Threaded PVC				
Timer		1	0	0
Trellis		2		
Valve Socket	2"	2		
Wire Ties		1 package		
Water Pump (ac/dc)	220 gph	2	$35	$70
Water Tubing (flexible)	10'	1	$5	$5

- The grow bed should be a bit larger than the tank and 4"-8" deep
- IBC is an Intermediate Bulk Container. It will be cut down and divided to be the grow bed and the fish tank. The size of IBC 48"L x 40"W x 54"H
- Water weighs 8.34# per gallon
- Learn how to skin and fillet tilapia fish
- Fill the grow bed completely with grow medium
- Place a tarp on the floor to cover the area of the garden and the water tanks

In addition to the aquaponics gardens, make a number of vertical hydroponic gardens. Here is the video: http://www.youtube.com/watch?v=wzbPBx9KiuM

SEEDS

GET SEEDS AND NUTRIENTS FROM www.burpee.com or Baker Creek, Southern Exposure. Keep extra seeds for barter. The more food you have growing, the longer you can survive, the better and cleaner the air and the more you have for barter. I prefer heirloom seeds, as their seeds are able to be planted. Hybrid seeds usually cannot be planted. Put all fruits in one IBC and all vegetables in the other. Some of these should be planted outside, for example, apple, cherry, orange and corn. The list below are the seeds I am stocking to make my own gardens.

If you want baby-corn, pick the top cobs early when they are small and about four to six inches in length.

(For Jews: since you are planting without dirt, you do not have to be concerned with *kilayim*. Confirm with your local *Posek*.)

Aloe
Arugula
Avocado
Baby Corn
Basil
Blueberry
Broccoli
Carrot
Celery
Chard
Cherry
Chive
Chocolate Mint
Collard
Cranberry
Cucumber
Dill
Endive
Fig
Garlic
Grape
Green Beans
Kale
Leek
Lemon
Mesculin
Mint
Onion

Orange
Oregano
Parsley
Peas
Peppers
Pineapple
Plum
Potato
Quinoa
Romaine
Rosemary
Sage
Scallion
Sea Weed
Snap Peas
Sour Sop
Soy
Spinach
Sprouts
Strawberry
Sunchoke (Jerusalem Artichoke)
Thyme
Tomato
Watercress
Wheatgrass

MINI AQUAPONICS SYSTEM

THE FOLLOWING CHART IS FOR a mini-aquaponics system (Robert Brennan). This system should hold about 4-6 fish per tank. You will need a small tank for birthing. This would be helpful if you want to have more fish than what I have delineated above.

SUPPLIES:
2 totes 8 to 12 inch deep (Home Depot $16 each)
6 ½ inch bulkheads (eBay $1 each)
2 ¾ inch PVC threaded pipe (Home Depot $6 each)
2 inch ABS pipe 3 feet long (Home Depot $7)
2 37 gallon totes (Home Depot $18 each)
½ inch tubing 10 feet (Home Depot $4)
½ inch clear tubing 10 feet (Home Depot $9)
½ inch threaded ball valve (Home Depot $5)
2 ½ inch threaded to pressure fit connector (Home Depot $1)
½ inch reducer (Home Depot $1)
1400 liter per hour submersible pump (eBay $6)
½ inch pressure fit T-joint connector (Home Depot $1)
2 x 50 liters of Hydroton (Hydroponics supply $36 each)
Total = $183

PREPAREDNESS CHECK LIST

THE following is a check list of things you should do at least on a weekly basis. I put it in a chart form so you can use it as an actual work sheet. Fill in the date and add a check mark in the box in the appropriate column. There is a .pdf version on the website you may download for free. www.doomsdaybunkerbook.com.

DATE																							
Animal Food																							
Barter Supplies																							
Bathroom																							
Batteries																							
Bee Hive																							
Booby Traps																							
Canned Goods																							
Clean Property																							
Compound																							

Border																					
Compound Lights																					
Down Spouts																					
Drone																					
Eggs																					
Extra NBC Filters																					
Faraday Cages (4)																					
Fences																					
Fire Starters																					
First Aid Supplies																					
Fish																					
Food Supply																					
Garden																					
Gasoline																					
Generator																					
Goat Food																					
Goat Security																					
Hen Food																					
Hen Security																					
IBC's																					
Kitty Liter																					
Loud Speaker																					
Medicine																					
Motor oil																					
NBC																					
Pet Food																					
Pet Supplies																					

Pill Boxes																					
Plant Food																					
Plants																					
Pond																					
Propane																					
Rain Gutters																					
Safe																					
Sawdust																					
Shut-off Valves																					
Solar Panels																					
Solar System																					
Solar Batteries																					
Speaker System																					
Surveillance Cameras																					
Tire Wall																					
Water Pitchers																					
Water Storage																					
Wood																					
Wood Pellets																					

Review the Radiation Protocols later in this book.

IN THE EVENT OF AN EMERGENCY

IN the event of an emergency, SHTF or TEOTWAWKI, the following is a list of some of the things you should do. This list is not all encompassing, however, it will give you a good start to make your own list for your own situation. There is a .pdf version on the website you may download for free. www.doomsdaybunkerbook.com.

1. Check bunker supply of wood
2. Check bunker supply of food
3. Check bunker supply of water
4. Check fence around the edge of the property
5. Activate all the outdoor underground traps
6. Activate all the outdoor aboveground traps
7. Check the pill boxes
8. Check the compound perimeter
9. Lock the compound gates
10. Check loud speaker system
11. Check the outdoor lighting system
12. Make sure all vehicles have full tanks of gas
13. Check the camouflage for the emergency hatch (door #9)
14. Check fire pit
15. Put the vehicles in the car ports
16. Make sure the vehicles are locked and alarmed

17. Check the water barrels in the hitch
18. Check all fluids in the RV
19. Lock down the car ports
20. Check rain gutters
21. Check downspouts
22. Put pets inside
23. Make sure the goats are secure
24. Make sure the goats have plenty of food and water
25. Make sure the hens are secure
26. Make sure the hens have plenty of food and water
27. Check and lock all fences
28. Check the pond
29. Check positioning of surveillance cameras
30. Confirm the solar panels are clear
31. Secure the generator
32. Put trip wire in front of the surface structure
33. Lock surface structure door (door 1)
34. Barricade surface structure door
35. Make sure the camouflage for the hatch (door 2) is prepared
36. Close the hatch
37. Lock the hatch
38. Set the electromagnetic lock
39. Secure the foam pad to the hatch
40. Activate the ramp shock battery
41. Put up the trip wire in the ramp
42. Lock the ramp door (door 3)
43. Secure the foam pad to the inside of door 3
44. Barricade the door
45. Make sure all water tanks are topped off
46. Check all water pitchers and containers
47. Turn off all incoming water
48. Disconnect all wires from the solar system to be able to completely close off the faraday cage
49. Secure faraday cage around battery bank
50. Lock the bunker door (door 4)
51. Secure the foam pad to the door
52. Barricade the door
53. Turn off all incoming air

54. Close off all incoming air pipes
55. Deposit all electronics (cell phones, weather station, backup hard drives, laptops, weather station, HT's, Ham radio,) into the faraday cages
56. Secure all faraday cages
57. Close off pellet stove and wood stove vents
58. Go into the emergency exit and make sure it is secure
59. Lock the hatch (door 9)
60. Check the electromagnetic lock
61. Attach a foam pad to the hatch
62. Make sure the shock battery is set up
63. Bubble wrap on the floor
64. Check the bug-out kits
65. Check the trip wire
66. Close the emergency exit door (door 8)
67. Lock the emergency exit door
68. Put a foam pad against the emergency exit door
69. Barricade the door
70. Basement, close off all incoming air vents
71. Check to make sure the safe is secure with its shielding
72. Lock the safe.
73. Close the basement door (door 7)
74. Bedroom: close off all incoming air vents
75. Turn on internal vent fan
76. Shut off incoming water
77. Check first aid and medical supplies
78. Close the bedroom door (door 6)
79. Close composting pit (door 10)
80. Close trash tube (door 11)
81. Close and lock door 5
82. Put a foam pad in front of the door
83. Barricade door 5
84. Check the drone
85. Check the surveillance monitors

EMP

AN EMP (electromagnetic pulse) attack would cause extensive and major damage on many levels. In fact, the higher in the atmosphere an EMP is detonated, the worse the effect. However, let us first explain what an EMP is, and then discuss some facts and fictions about them and then finally what you can do to protect yourself.

This chapter is gleaned from numerous sources including electrical engineering experts.

The EMP or electromagnetic pulse was discovered after early nuclear tests knocked out power and communications systems many miles from the test site. Every nuclear blast emits EMP's. The government has conducted extensive research on EMP's, however since the cold-war ended, research has been cut back and much of the information is still classified. Hence, the actual knowledge of specific effects of an EMP attack are scarce and most of what we "know" is conjecture. It is generally accepted that a major EMP attack would cause severe damage to our national infrastructure and to our own personal electronics.

An EMP attack would most likely occur as a powerful, high-altitude, nuclear blast over the central United States. Rogue nations with limited capabilities such as North Korea or Iran may soon be able to launch an effective EMP attack. Other devices, called e-bombs, some of which can be constructed with conventional explosives and easily obtained electrical components, present a more localized threat. The prevention is the same for e-bombs.

EMP is similar to a radio wave in that it will penetrate some materials easily and be blocked or attenuated by others. There are two parts to an EMP. The first is the initial blast that will travel through the air in a line-of-sight pattern. The second part of an EMP blast will be a slightly delayed pulse that will arrive over the power lines, phone lines and cable lines. These lines will conduct a great deal of EMP energy because they will act as very long antennas. This energy will then be dumped into your power outlets and phone jacks destroying most of the electronics connected to them. External antennas will also absorb EMP energy and the larger the antenna, the more it will absorb. Any large metal structure will collect or absorb EMP energy; if it is grounded such as a water tower might be, then the energy will dissipate into the earth.

The amount of damage caused by an EMP will depend on several factors; The power of the EMP device(s), the amount of shielding between the electronics and the EMP source, and how delicate the electronics are. Semiconductors and microcircuit chips are the most susceptible. EMP will damage your electronics even if they are turned off because the EMP introduces an electrical current into any conductor it hits and in a matter of only a few microseconds it can burn out sensitive circuits.

The effects of an EMP attack could be haphazard, taking out some things and missing others. Partial shielding in steel framed or sided buildings or metal bodied cars could mean less damage to the electronics than in a wood

EMP

framed house or a fiberglass bodied car. Your car may survive due to its metal body, but that shielding has gaps, so maybe it will not. It is impossible to predict. Also where the car is located when the EMP attack occurs will have an effect. The electronics may be temporarily disabled and recover at least partially after the excess electrical charge dissipates, but maybe not. Older cars without electronic ignition will probably be fine. Even if your cell phone survives it will be useless because satellites and ground stations will not work. The exact affects are difficult to predict, as there are too many variables.

The good news is that it is fairly easy and inexpensive to protect your survival electronics from EMP damage by using what is known as a faraday cage. The idea is to get a metal (or other conductive metal) container. Whatever is inside of the closed container would be shielded. The next step would be to put some foam, rubber, cardboard or other non-conducting material inside the container, sit the electronics in the insulation, close the lid and you have some protection from EMP. Put that container inside your metal gun cabinet or file cabinet and not touching the metal of the cabinet and now you have even more protection. It is all about shielding.

The faraday cage or shielding is best if it is made from a continuous fairly thick metal enclosure that is a very good conductor of electricity such as copper or aluminum. Ideally it should have no holes or gaps in its surface and all sides should make electrical contact. That would be the ideal shield, but a lesser shield may be more quickly produced and offer sufficient EMP protection to withstand a less severe attack.

A washer or dryer could be used in a pinch if it has metal on all sides, top and bottom. A microwave oven would offer only minimal protection because the screen shield used in the front window which is tuned to filter out the microwave from **inside** the oven, not incoming EMP.

As a last resort if nothing else is available and attack seems eminent, wrapping a cardboard box in several layers of aluminum foil is better than no shielding at all.

Faraday cages can be as small or as large as needed. An entire house could be shielded or just your cell phone. A small faraday cage for EMP protection does not need to be grounded. Keep in mind the grounds in the electrical system of a house or even cold water pipes could possibly become charged if the attack is very strong, so those would not work. For larger structures such as a garage or house, a good proper **exclusive** earth grounding rod would be recommended.

Always remove batteries from any device, and unplug everything from wall outlets. Turning off your electronics alone will not be sufficient.

In the case of an EMP attack, look for wide spread outages of essential services; The power grid may be out for a long time, police and emergency services could be severely hampered. Hospitals may lose essential medical devices, radio stations may be off the air, phone communications and traffic controls could be disabled for a long time.

In the event of such an EMP attack, the HAM radio operators who are knowledgeable about protection from EMP will be an invaluable resource. It is imperative that your emergency radio receivers have short wave bands so you can tune in and listen for vital information the HAM operators may be passing over the air waves. Also with these radios you can listen to news reports from around the world. The radios should be battery, solar and even hand-crank powered. Remember the power grid may not be functioning.

Devices such as lightning arrestors or surge protectors that are rated by their manufacturer to protect against EMP are probably a good investment. However, since we have never had an actual EMP attack these devices are unproven in real world scenarios. Remember, shielding is a big part of the equation and those devices may not protect you from the airborne pulse (the initial pulse) striking your electronics directly. When looking at specifications for EMI (Electromagnetic Interference) or RFI (Radio Frequency Interference) shielding, remember this shielding is not adequate for EMP although it may mitigate damage to a small degree in some cases.

The bottom line is: If it is essential survival electronics, keep it adequately shielded and disconnected from external cables and antennas and remove any batteries. This way it stands a better chance to be available when you need it most.

MYTHS

MYTH #1: Mylar bags and wraps will protect your electronics from EMP.

WRONG: EMP will go right through Mylar, unless it has a metallic coating or is metalized especially with EMP shielding. Simple anti-static bags will not be adequate at all. Make sure you have the right type.

MYTH #2: Faraday shields or cages must be grounded in order to protect from EMP.

WRONG: Not only do they not have to be grounded, grounding them could actually make the situation worse. The EMP pulse or pulses will induce a current flow in most of the grounding wires in most ordinary buildings making them a potential source of EMP damage.

MYTH #3: Turning off your electronics offers no protection from EMP.

WRONG: Turning off electronic devices may offer some minor protection but certainly not complete protection. It is less likely to be damaged if it is off, however, it can indeed be damaged either way. If you cannot shield it in a faraday cage, you should make sure it is off and unplugged from the wall outlet or external cables or antennas and shielded as well as possible perhaps inside a metal cabinet or something similar.

MYTH #4: 90% of the population will die within a year of a massive EMP attack.

WRONG: Although many will undoubtedly perish, there is no evidence that an EMP will directly cause death to large groups of people. More people are likely to die from riots and loss of medical care, than from an EMP.

MYTH #5: Burying the electronics in the ground will protect them.

WRONG: An EMP attack will penetrate the ground to some extent depending on how strong the pulse is, how deep the electronics are and the type of soil. A very deep hole may work, a cave could be adequate if enough rock is between you and the pulse. An underground bunker ten feet deep should be more than adequate. However, even inside a deep bunker or cave, I still suggest using faraday cages.

MYTH #6: An EMP attack would wipe out the entire power grid.

WRONG: This would actually depend on the type of EMP attack, the power of the bomb and how high it was detonated.

MYTH #7: A microwave oven makes a good shield from EMP.

WRONG: It might help to a small degree if you have nothing else but the microwave shielding is not broad enough to block out the full spectrum of the EMP burst.

MYTH #8: You can use a cell phone or radio receiver to test a faraday cage's shielding ability.

WRONG: This would only prove that very weak signals cannot penetrate the shield. An EMP burst is huge compared to ordinary radio waves and may very easily penetrate any cage that blocked the mere radio signals. Without a testing facility, there is no way to know for sure.

MYTH #9: It is not necessary to insulate the inside of a faraday cage because the effect of electromagnetic radio frequency radiation will not penetrate to the inside of the metal shield due to the phenomenon known as the "skin effect".

WRONG: This may be true of ordinary levels of radiation. An EMP attack will generate far greater levels of radiation that will penetrate to the inner level of the shield.

FARADAY CAGE

AFTER reading the previous chapter, you may be wondering why I am including a chapter on how to make a faraday cage. Living in a deep underground bunker should protect you and your devices from an EMP. The reason for the inclusion of this chapter is quite simple: No one knows for sure what exactly is needed to shield from an EMP. Having your devices in an underground bunker will probably protect you, however, it would still be a good idea to make a faraday cage. Also, do not forget, you have electronics on the surface, for example, your speaker, lights, solar panels and much more. I want to help you be as protected as possible.

The following is how to make a simple faraday cage. I suggest making several of these to have a decent amount of space for electronics. A faraday cage is used to protect electronics in the case of a solar flare or an EMP from a neutron bomb or a nuclear bomb. My idea is to build four faraday cages:

1. Around the solar electrical system - storage area 44
2. For office equipment - storage area 51
3. Emergency electronic equipment - storage area 123

4. Safe - storage area 124

The only two requirements for protection with a faraday cage are:

1. The equipment inside the box does NOT touch the metal container (plastic, wadded paper, foam or cardboard can all be used to insulate it from the metal)
2. The metal shield is continuous without any gaps between pieces or large holes in it.

Grounding a faraday cage is NOT necessary and in some cases actually may be less than ideal.

Purchase a steel (or other conductive type – aluminum) garbage can or large box. A garbage can may be purchased from Home Depot or Lowes for about $25. This is all I could find: Only about 14" tall:

http://www.homedepot.com/p/TCG-Galvanized-Charcoal-or-Ash-Can-with-Lid-SR8012/203147413?N=Zbx82%2FNtk-Extended%2FNtt-garbage%252Bcan#.Upfo9uKOmSo

Get some cardboard. Cut the cardboard to fit the top and bottom snugly. Cut the cardboard to fit the inside walls of the garbage can. Put it all together and add tape where necessary.

Another great idea is a metal trunk. This one already has wood on the inside to act as shielding. Size - 30" L x 16" W x 12 1/2" H:

http://www.campbound.com/Small-Camp-Trunk-Red.aspx?gclid=CKvkso-e2r4CFUOFOgodkBMACQ

For added protection, make a nested faraday cage. This is done by taking some electronics and putting them inside a faraday cage. Then place this inside of a larger faraday cage. Basically, you are putting a faraday cage inside of a faraday cage.

Another suggestion is to find a large steel box to put your laptops inside. Get several of these boxes and line all six sides with cardboard.

In the safe, place a backup hard drive, maybe a small amount of cash and all important papers (passports, birth certificates, marriage license, property deed, etc.).

GASIFIER

WHAT is a gasifier? I am so glad you asked. There is an old process, one you probably do not know much about, that is gaining popularity and may join wind, solar and hydropower in the pantheon of clean, renewable energy. The process is known as **gasification**, a set of chemical reactions that uses limited oxygen to convert a carbon-containing feedstock (organic waste) into a **synthetic gas**, or **syngas**.

It sounds like combustion, but it is not. Combustion uses an abundance of oxygen to produce heat and light by burning. Gasification uses only a very small amount of oxygen, which is combined with steam and cooked under intense pressure. This initiates a series of reactions that produces a gaseous mixture composed primarily of carbon monoxide and hydrogen. This syngas can be burned directly or used as a starting point to manufacture fertilizers, pure hydrogen, methane or liquid transportation fuels.

SAFETY EQUIPMENT
Safety glasses
Ear plugs
Face shield

TOOLS
Tape measure
Crescent wrench
Cotton gloves
Leather gloves
Angle grinder w/1 regular wheel and 2 cut off wheels
Drill and 1/2 inch drill bit
Lenox 2 inch hole saw
Fine file (optional)
Welder

SPECIAL TOOL
For use with gasifier operation: CDN grill surface thermometer GTS800

PARTS
- 55 gal. metal drum
- (1) 120mm ammo can
- (1) 40mm ammo can
- 6 feet of 2 inch high temperature 2 ply hose part# 3631-2.00- 6 FOOT may be purchased at this website: https://www.pegasusautoracing.com/pro
- 17" of expanded metal or heavy screen (for holding grid for filter media)
- (2) pipe clamps 2 1/4 to 1 5/16 inch
- (1)1/2 inch hose to 1/2 inch thread
- (1) 2inch pipe that is 3inchs long
- (1)2inch pipe that is 6inchs long
- (1) red rtv silicone (Napa part num#81160)
- Shredded cardboard and paper for filter media

GENERATOR MODIFICATION PARTS

NOTE: Your generator may be different and require different plumbing to carburetor
- (3) 1/2 inch hose to 1/2 inch thread

- 6 feet of 1/2 inch high temp hose (rated to 200 degrees)
- 1/2 inch tee threaded male on 2 ends and female on 1
- 1/2 inch ball valve
- 1/2 inch thread to thread nipple
- half inch union

This should be a complete parts list. For detailed instructions on how to build this, go to:
http://www.allselfsustained.com/generate-electricity-from-waste/

BUG OUT KIT

THE bug-out kits will be stored on the emergency exit ramp in storage area 69. Have at least one bug-out kit per person, have an additional one for each animal. A bug-out kit should not weigh more than twenty-five percent of one's weight. This weight restriction will help prevent fatigue over the long haul. Each bug-out kit should include as much food as possible and the following:

ITEM	#
4-in-1 Dynamo Flashlight	1
5-in-1 Survival Whistle	1
50 ft. Paracord	1
Change of Clothes	1
Duffle Bag on Wheels	1
Fork, Knife, Spoon, Cup	1
Glow Sticks	2
Hand Warmers	2
Large Candle	1
Medicine (Doses)	30
NIOSH N95 Dust Masks	2
Note Pad	1
Pencil	1
Pocket Tissue Packs	4

BUG OUT KIT

Rain Poncho	1
Sleeping Bag	1
Swiss Army Knife	1
Waste Bags	2
Water Bottles	3
Water Proof Matches (50)	1
Water Purification Tablets	1
Wipes	1
Work Gloves	1

Split the following between each bug-out kit

ITEM	#
Collapsible Shovel	1
Compass	1
Can Opener	1
First Aid Kit	1
Pup Tent	1

BARTER

THE following is a list of suggested items to keep on hand for bartering. Keep some of these items in the appropriate storage areas and the rest in storage area 99. Cash money, credit cards, checks, precious metals and jewels will have no value. The only items of any value are items that will be able to be used by other people. Food, water and medicine can be used as barter. Stock up for yourselves before stocking up for barter.

Unfortunately, in times of distress, some people will take advantage of others. I have two things to say about this:

1. Do not be of those who take advantage of others in difficult times. There will be enough trouble in the world, we do not need to add to it.
2. Be careful of those who would take advantage of others in difficult times.

Keep in mind that physical items are not the only things you may be able to barter. Your **knowledge** is also something you can barter. Much of what you have learned in this book, and the supplements from the website are also things you can barter.

BARTER ITEMS

Alcohol
Ammunition
Antibiotics
Baking Soda
Batteries
Bleach
Bolts
Candles
Cigarettes
Coffee
Coffee Creamer
Condiments
Drop Cloth
Duct Tape
Eggs
Emergency Blankets
Feminine Products
First Aid Supplies
Fishing Supplies
Flashlights
Floss
Food
Fuel
Goat Milk
Hand Tools
Hand Warmers
Hard Candy
Honey
Knives (Various Sizes)
Matches
Milk
Neosporin

Nuts
Pain Killers
Paper
Paracord
Pepper Spray
Petroleum Jelly
Plant Seeds
Propane
Razor Blades
Rope, Nylon
Salt
Seasonings
Seeds
Sewing Supplies
Shampoo
Soap
Sugar
Tarps
Tea
Toilet Paper
Tooth Brush
Toothpaste
Trash Bags
Vinegar
Vodka
Washers
Water
Water Purification Tablets
Waterless Soap
Wire Ties
Yoghurt
Zip Lock Bags

BARTER SERVICES

Ability to charge batteries

Baking
Buck stud services
Computer repair
Construction
Cooking
Hunting
Making a candle heater
Making a rocket stove
Making a Zeer fridge
Making candles
Medical knowledge
Sewing
Skinning
Welding

FIRST AID SUPPLIES

FIRST aid supplies should be stored in storage area 19. Get as many and as much of these supplies as possible for emergencies, and for barter. Where possible, get assorted sizes.

2" & 3" Sterile Roll
Bandages
Activated Charcoal
Adhesive Tape
Afrin
Antacid
Anti-Diarrhea Medication
Antiseptic
Antiseptic Spray
Aspirin
Baby Oil
Blood Pressure Cuff
Braces
Cotton Balls
Crutches
Cleansing Agent/Soap
Cold-Eze
Cotton Swabs
Dayquil

Essential Oils
Eye Drops
Eye Wash
Folding Splints
Glucose Monitoring Kit
Hydrogen Peroxide
IV Bags
Latex Gloves
Laxative
Lozenges
Lice Shampoo
Massage Oils
Medication
Neosporin
Non-Aspirin Pain Reliever
Nyquil
Petroleum Jelly
Potassium Iodide
Rubbing Alcohol

Safety Glasses
Safety Pins
Safety Razor Blade
Saline Solution
Scalpels
Scissors
Smelling Salts
Splints
Sterile Adhesive Bandages
Sterile Gauze Pads
Straight Pins
Sweet Almond Oil
Syrup of Ipecac
Thermometer
Tongue Blades
Triangular Bandages
Tweezers
Vitamins
Wooden Applicator Sticks

Purchase extra eyewear (glasses, contacts, contact solution), dentures, denture glue, sunglasses

Potassium Iodide is used to protect the thyroid in case of a nuclear bomb

Leeches - *Macrobdella decora* http://www.leeches.biz/ figure about $8 per leech plus shipping of $25

Get a portable hospital kit for $500.
http://www.cheaperthandirt.com/product/MHR-316#

Tick and flee medicine for your dog.

MEDICAL TIPS

BEFORE you sequester yourself in your bunker, make sure all your medical tests are up to date. Make sure your teeth and health are in good order as it may be a while until you will be able to do so again. Take care of your health, eat well and exercise. Keep your brain in gear and do things to stimulate yourself both physically, spiritually and mentally. It is your physical, spiritual and mental health that will sustain you. If you are on prescription medication, make sure you have enough to last you for a while inside the bunker. Every month, put aside one pill and reserve it. Rotate your inventory. Do NOT buy illegal drugs, you will get caught and go to jail.

You are going to want to live off the grid. You will need to be able to take care of your health. This is one of the reasons I have taken the time to write several pages herein about health. During times of stress, we need to take better care of ourselves as our immune systems are compromised. We have also learned that living in a time of SHTF or TEOTWAWKI, cash money will be worthless. We have also learned you should stock up on barter items. However, being knowledgeable about medical issues is also something you can barter. Learn first aid and CPR.

This chapter is full of alternative medicine tips, however, there is so much more information available on the Internet. Get a few books on alternative medical procedures, acupressure for the lay person and first aid books.

These statements have not been evaluated by the Food and Drug Administration. This information is not intended to diagnose, treat, cure, or prevent any disease.

BLOOD THINNERS:

- Natural vitamin E – 100 IUs of **natural** (not synthetic) vitamin E is at least as effective as aspirin, according to some research.
- Ginkobiloba – ginko has been used for centuries to inhibit clotting and improve circulation
- Water – yes, it sounds like a cop-out but water is the best natural blood thinner there is.

ANTI-INFLAMMATORIES:

- Devil's claw – this has been used as an anti-inflammatory and pain killer for successful treatment of arthritis, tendonitis and muscle pain.
- Turmeric – used for pain and inflammation.
- Ginger – pain and inflammation

STATINS

Statins, including Lipitor and Zocor, are used to lower cholesterol in order to avoid heart attacks and cardiovascular disease. There are many natural alternatives to these medications you can use now and in the case of a survivalist, SHTF scenario.

- Red wine – the resveratrol and other antioxidants in red wine work well to keep cholesterol down.
- Garlic
- Olive oil (those omega-3's again!)
- Fiber-rich foods such as oats and vegetables

- Dark chocolate in moderation
- Coconut oil and other medium-chain triglycerides instead of regular fats that can raise bad (LDL) cholesterol

BLOOD PRESSURE

Though high blood pressure can be genetic, it is mostly a dietary issue. However, once developed, it is a life-threatening condition requiring daily treatment. In addition to losing weight, there are some natural remedies that work as natural blood pressure medications in a survivalist SHTF scenario. Even if you do not have high blood pressure, you should get a portable blood pressure tester. They are inexpensive and good to have around.

- Increase potassium. Bananas, potatoes, tomato juice and coconut water are all high in potassium, which can help lower blood pressure.
- Coenzyme Q10 works well to lower blood pressure
- Garlic
- Hawthorn
- Foods containing magnesium and calcium
- REDUCE sodium intake. This directly affects your blood pressure!
- Walk and exercise
- Drink as much water as possible

ANTACIDS

Heart burn, acid reflux and stomach upset do not have to plague you, even in a SHTF situation. When you are making your survivalist list, include these natural alternatives to antacids.

- Almonds – they naturally reduce stomach acid. Take a handful of fifteen to twenty and your heartburn will disappear in a half-hour or so.
- Aloe Vera juice – long used to heal ulcers and soothe upset stomachs. If you are making your

own, follow proper procedure. Aloe is very easy to grow.

- Apple cider vinegar – though it may sound counterproductive to throw acid on heartburn, apple cider vinegar has been used forever to cure stomach ailments. Stir two tablespoons into a few ounces of water and drink it immediately following a meal.
- Apples – a slice of apple can reduce stomach acid and have you feeling better in five minutes or so.
- Baking soda – mix a teaspoon in a few ounce of water and drink. Do not use it regularly though because it can increase sodium levels.
- Bananas
- Basil leaves – 2-3 will do the trick.
- Buttermilk
- Chamomile
- Cinnamon
- Fennel
- Garlic
- Ginger
- Grapes
- Peppermint

The list for natural antacids goes on and on but these are some of the best.

TYPE-2 DIABETES

Though there is no real approved alternative treatment for type-2 diabetes, there are some interesting research studies taking place that suggest the following may be effective in helping to control it. In a SHTF situation, an alternative treatment for diabetes may be necessary, so having these on hand certainly cannot hurt. Also, it should go without saying any food that raises glucose levels should be eaten with extreme care.

- North American ginseng – may help with blood sugar control and glycosylated hemoglobin levels.

- Chromium – this essential trace mineral plays an important role in carbohydrate and fat metabolism and helps cells respond correctly to insulin.
- Magnesium – found naturally in green leafy vegetables, nuts, seeds and grains. It is an essential mineral for everything from blood sugar metabolism to sodium uptake.
- Cinnamon – studies are showing as little as 1 gram or as much as 6 grams of cinnamon may improve blood glucose control in people with type-2 diabetes.

PAIN KILLERS

There are two primary types of natural anesthetics: Topical and internal. Topical anesthetics are used directly on your skin, and internal anesthetics are ingested and work from the inside out. You want to use a topical anesthetic to treat issues such as toothaches, cuts, rashes, and burns. Internal anesthetics are used to treat conditions such as general pain, headaches and muscle aches. Since anything taken internally can quickly kill you, we are going to stick to topical anesthetics.

CLOVE OIL
Clove oil has been used for centuries to relieve toothaches and now studies show it is basically as effective as benzocaine for topically numbing pain.

You can make a gel with it or simply dab some of the oil straight onto your gum and let it sit. Keep in mind this is only going to numb your tooth, not cure the problem. You are eventually going to need to take care of the bad tooth that is causing the pain because the infection can spread to your heart and kill you.

Clove oil can also be used to relieve itching and burning related to dry skin, poison ivy and poison oak. It is also used to treat upset stomach but you need to know how much to take because high doses are toxic.

CAYENNE PEPPER

In addition to many other health benefits, the capsaicin in cayenne pepper is also great to use to treat arthritis, bursitis, psoriasis, eczema, muscle pain, and nerve pain.

Capsaicin is the chemical in peppers that makes them hot. However when used topically, it causes your body to release a chemical called Substance P. This is the chemical that carries pain messages from your nerves to your brain.

In addition to capsaicin, cayenne also contains salicylates, the same compounds found in aspirin.

The best way to apply the cayenne to your skin is to make a gel or cream out of it using coconut oil or other natural bases. When you first apply it, you will feel hot. That is because the capsaicin is causing the Substance P to flood through. Once your supply is depleted within a couple of minutes, you will get relief.

LAVENDER

This pretty purple flower has been used for centuries as an antiseptic, topical anesthetic and sedative and is safe for use on your pets, too. You will often find it as an ingredient in essential oils created for relaxation or to treat insomnia.

It is great to treat cuts and scrapes too because in addition to relieving the pain, it also helps prevent scarring and stop bleeding.

If you make a lavender salve, you can rub it on your muscles and joints to relieve sprains and other muscle pain as well as cramps and sore feet.

WINTERGREEN

Wintergreen is a mild anesthetic that is good to treat toothaches or stomach aches, but since it is so easy to grow, I thought I would throw it in.

Other anesthetics that have been used throughout history include onions, garlic, ginger, tea tree oil, and Epsom salts.

Peppermint and apple cider vinegar are typical natural remedies for upset stomach and other digestive issues. Calendula, Jasmine, Yarrow and Chamomile are great for relieving itching caused by just about anything and can also help with inflammation.

Bach Flower Remedies http://www.directlyfromnature.com/

CILANTRO

Cilantro is a powerful natural cleansing agent. Cilantro can be used to help remove heavy metals and other toxic agents from the body.

The chemical compounds in cilantro actually bind to the heavy metals, loosening them from the tissues, blood and organs. Cilantro then transports these harmful substances out of the body through elimination.

Cilantro is also good to help people who have been exposed to heightened levels of toxins and mercury. However, one would need to consume large amounts of cilantro over a long period of time.

The rich qualities of cilantro oil have a powerfully positive effect on our digestive tract. The oils aid our digestive system in its production of digestive enzymes, acids and juices.

The known benefits of cilantro are extensive:

- Powerful anti-inflammatory capacities that may help symptoms of arthritis
- Protective against bacterial infection from salmonella
- Acts to increase HDL cholesterol (the good kind)
- Helps reduce LDL cholesterol (the bad kind)
- Relief for stomach gas
- Prevention of flatulence
- Digestive aid
- Wards off urinary tract infections
- Helps reduce feelings of nausea
- Eases hormonal mood swings associated with menstruation
- Has been shown to reduce menstrual cramping.
- Adds fiber to the digestive tract
- A source of iron, magnesium, and is helpful in fighting anemia
- Gives relief for diarrhea, especially if caused by microbial or fungal infections
- Helps promote healthy liver function.
- Reduces minor swelling
- Strong general antioxidant
- Disinfects and helps detoxify the body
- Stimulates the endocrine glands
- Helps with insulin secretion and lowers blood sugar
- Acts as a natural anti-septic and anti-fungal agent for skin disorders like fungal infections and eczema
- Contains immune-boosting properties
- Acts as an expectorant
- Helps ease conjunctivitis, as well as eye-aging, macular degeneration, and other stressors on the eyes

HOT PEPPERS

Most people do not like hot peppers. I know that I sure do not like them. However, hot peppers do have some great uses. I will give you just a few. You could pickle, cook, roast, dehydrate, etc.

Hot peppers are a great cleanser for the body. They will help in removing bacteria and viruses. I will often drink a tea I make from hot peppers. In the rare time that I get a cold of flu, I drink about eight to ten cups of this tea per day and the cold is gone in just one or two days.

Fill the largest pot you have (I use a twenty quart stock pot) with water. Into the water, toss about thirty hot peppers. Add some fresh lemon juice from several lemons. Let this simmer for a few hours. Pour yourself a steaming cup and add as much honey as you like.

CINNAMON AND HONEY

DRUG companies will not like this getting around. This chapter is taken (with permission) from www.yourkosherchef.com.

These statements have not been evaluated by the Food and Drug Administration. This information is not intended to diagnose, treat, cure, or prevent any disease.

It has been found that a mix of **pure** honey and cinnamon can help with many diseases. Honey is produced in most countries of the world. Scientists of today also note honey as very effective medicine for all kinds of diseases. Honey can be used without side effects which is also a plus. Today's science says, even though honey is sweet, when it is taken in the right dosage as a medicine, it does not harm even diabetic patients. Researched by western scientists:

ARTHRITIS: Arthritis patients can benefit by taking one cup of hot water with two tablespoons of honey and one small teaspoon of cinnamon powder. When taken daily even chronic arthritis may be cured. In research conducted at the Copenhagen University, it was found when doctors treated their patients with a mixture of one tablespoon honey and half teaspoon cinnamon powder before breakfast, they found within a week (out of the 200 people so treated) 73 patients were totally relieved of pain -- and within a month, almost all the patients who could not walk or move around because of arthritis, now started walking without pain.

BAD BREATH: People of South America, gargle with one teaspoon of honey and cinnamon powder mixed in hot water first thing in the morning so their breath stays fresh throughout the day.

BLADDER INFECTIONS: Take two tablespoons of cinnamon powder and one teaspoon of honey in a glass of lukewarm water and drink it. It destroys the germs in the bladder.

CHOLESTEROL: Two tablespoons of honey and three teaspoons of cinnamon powder mixed in sixteen ounces of tea water given to a cholesterol patient was found to reduce the level of cholesterol in the blood by ten percent within two hours. When taken three times a day, any chronic cholesterol, could be cured. Pure honey taken with daily food relieves high cholesterol.

COLDS: Those suffering from common or severe colds should take one tablespoon lukewarm honey with 1/4 teaspoon cinnamon powder daily for three days. This process will cure most chronic coughs, colds and clear the sinuses.

FATIGUE: Recent studies have shown, the sugar content of honey is more helpful, rather than being detrimental, to the strength of the body. Senior citizens who take honey and cinnamon powder in equal parts are more alert and flexible. Dr. Milton, who has done research, says a half tablespoon of honey taken in a glass of water and sprinkled with cinnamon powder, even when the vitality of the body starts to decrease, when taken daily after brushing your teeth and in the afternoon at about 3:00 P.M., the vitality of the body increases within a week.

GAS: According to studies done in India and Japan, it was revealed when honey is taken with cinnamon powder, the stomach is relieved of gas.

HEARING LOSS: Daily morning and night honey and cinnamon powder, taken in equal parts, restores hearing.

HEART DISEASES: Make a paste of honey and cinnamon powder, put it on toast instead of jelly or jam and eat it regularly for breakfast. It reduces the cholesterol and could potentially save one from heart attack. Even if you have already had an attack, studies show you could avoid having another attack. Regular use of cinnamon and honey strengthens the heart beat. In America and Canada, various nursing homes have treated patients successfully and have found as one ages the arteries and veins lose their flexibility and get clogged; honey and cinnamon revitalize the arteries and the veins.

IMMUNE SYSTEM: Daily use of honey and cinnamon powder strengthens the immune system and protects the body from bacterial and viral attacks. Scientists have found honey has various vitamins and iron in large amounts. Constant use of honey strengthens the white blood corpuscles (where DNA is contained) to fight bacterial and viral diseases.

INDIGESTION: Cinnamon powder sprinkled on two tablespoons of honey taken before food is eaten relieves acidity and digests the heaviest of meals.

INFLUENZA: A scientist in Spain has proved that honey contains a natural "ingredient" which kills the influenza germs and saves the patient from flu.

LONGEVITY: Tea made with honey and cinnamon powder, when taken regularly, arrests the ravages of old age. Use four teaspoons of honey, one teaspoon of cinnamon powder, and three cups of boiling water to make a tea. Drink 1/4 cup, three to four times a day. It keeps the skin fresh and soft and arrests old age.

PIMPLES: Three tablespoons of honey and one teaspoon of cinnamon powder paste. Apply this paste on pimples before sleeping and wash it off the next morning with warm water. When done daily for two weeks, it removes all pimples from the root.

RASPY OR SORE THROAT: When your throat has a tickle or is raspy, take one tablespoon of honey in hot water and sip until gone. Repeat every three hours until your throat is without symptoms.

SKIN INFECTIONS: Applying honey and cinnamon powder in equal parts on the affected parts, cures eczema, ringworm and all types of skin infections.

UPSET STOMACH: Honey taken with cinnamon powder cures stomach ache and also is said to clear stomach ulcers from its root.

WEIGHT LOSS: Daily in the morning one half hour before breakfast and on an empty stomach, and at night before sleeping, drink honey and cinnamon powder boiled in one cup of water. When taken regularly, it reduces the weight of even the most obese person. Also, drinking this mixture regularly does not allow the fat to accumulate in the body even though the person may eat a high calorie diet.

NUCLEAR BLAST PROTOCALS

MUCH of this chapter has been gleaned from ready.gov. Most of this should sound familiar, as much of the information has already been mentioned elsewhere in this book. Some of the information in this chapter is irrelevant if you are living in a bunker, however you should know it in case you are not in your bunker at the time.

A nuclear blast is a powerful explosion with intense light, heat, a damaging pressure wave, and widespread radioactive material that will contaminate the air, water, and ground surfaces for many miles. A nuclear device can range from a weapon carried by an intercontinental missile launched by a hostile nation or terrorist organization, to a small portable nuclear device transported by an individual in a briefcase. All nuclear devices cause deadly effects when exploded, including blinding light, intense heat (thermal radiation), initial nuclear radiation, blast, fires started by the heat pulse and secondary fires caused by the destruction.

The three factors for protecting oneself from radiation and fallout are **Distance**, **Shielding** and **Time**.

DISTANCE

The more distance between you and the fallout particles, the better. Depending on the strength of the nuclear device, if you are within five miles of a nuclear blast, you are probably dead or dying and there is nothing you can do.

An underground area such as a home basement or office building basement offers more protection than the first floor of a building. A floor near the middle of a high-rise may be better, depending on what is nearby at that level on which significant fallout particles would collect. Flat roofs collect fallout particles so the top floor is not a good choice, nor is a floor adjacent to a neighboring flat roof. Can we say, "Underground bunker"?

SHIELDING

The heavier and denser the materials - thick walls, concrete, bricks, books and earth - between you and the fallout particles, the better. Can we say, "Underground bunker"?

TIME

Fallout radiation loses its intensity fairly rapidly. In time, you will be able to leave the fallout shelter. Radioactive fallout poses the greatest threat to people during the first two weeks, by which time it has declined to about one percent of its initial radiation level.

Remember, any protection, however temporary, is better than none at all, and the more **Distance, Shielding** and **Time** you can take advantage of, the better.

BEFORE THE BLAST

The following are things you can do to protect yourself, your family and your property in the event of a nuclear blast.

- Build an emergency supply kit, which includes non-perishable food, water, a battery-powered or hand-crank radio, extra flashlights and batteries. You may want to prepare a kit for your workplace and a portable kit to keep in your car in case you are told to evacuate.
- Make a family emergency plan. Your family may not be together when disaster strikes, so it is important to know how you will contact one another, how you will get back together, where you will meet and what you will do in case of an emergency.
- Plan places where your family will meet, both within and outside of your immediate neighborhood.
- Know your community's warning systems and disaster plans, including evacuation routes.
- Find out from officials if any public buildings in your community have been designated as fallout shelters. If none have been designated, make your own list of potential shelters near your home, workplace and school.
- These places would include basements or the windowless center area of middle floors in high-rise buildings, as well as subways and tunnels.
- If you live in an apartment building or high-rise, talk to the manager about the safest place in the building for sheltering and about providing for building occupants until it is safe to exit.
- During periods of heightened threat, increase your disaster supplies to be adequate for at least a month.

Taking shelter during a nuclear blast is absolutely necessary. There are two kinds of shelters - **Blast** and **Fallout**.

BLAST SHELTERS are specifically constructed to offer some protection against blast pressure, initial radiation, heat and fire. But even a blast shelter cannot withstand a direct hit from a nuclear explosion.

FALLOUT SHELTERS do not need to be specially constructed for protecting against fallout. They can be any protected space, provided the walls and roof are thick and dense enough to absorb the radiation given off by fallout particles.

DURING A NUCLEAR BLAST

The following are guidelines for what to do in the event of a nuclear explosion.

- Listen for official information and follow the instructions provided by emergency response personnel. Based on what is known about the threat, you may be asked to take shelter, go to a specific location or evacuate the area.
- If an attack warning is issued, take cover as quickly as feasible, below ground if possible, and stay there until instructed to do otherwise.
- Find the nearest building, preferably built of brick or concrete, and go inside to avoid any radioactive material outside.
- If a better shelter, such as a multi-story building or basement can be reached within a few minutes, go there immediately.
- Go as far below ground as possible or in the center of a tall building. The goal is to put as many walls and as much concrete, brick and soil between you and the radioactive material outside (think bunker).
- Stay where you are, even if you are separated from your family. Inside is the safest place for everyone in the impacted area. It can save your life.
- During the time with the highest radiation levels it is safest to stay inside, sheltered away from the radioactive material outside.

- Radiation levels are extremely dangerous after a nuclear detonation but the levels reduce rapidly.
- Expect to stay inside for at least twenty-four hours unless told otherwise by authorities.
- When evacuating is in your best interest, you will be instructed to do so. All available methods of communication will be used to provide news and / or instructions.
- People in the path of the radioactive material - downwind from the detonation - may also be asked to take protective measures.

If you are caught outside and unable to get inside immediately:

- Do not look at the flash or fireball - it can blind you.
- Take cover behind anything that might offer protection.
- Lie flat on the ground on your stomach and cover your head, even if it is just with your own hands.
- If the explosion is some distance away, it could take thirty seconds or more for the blast wave to hit.
- Turn your head away from the blast
- Cross your legs
- Take shelter as soon as you can, even if you are many miles from ground zero where the attack occurred. Radioactive fallout can be carried by the winds for hundreds of miles. Remember the three protective factors: Distance, Shielding and Time.
- If you were outside during or after the blast, get clean as soon as possible, to remove radioactive material that may have settled on your body.
  - Remove all your clothing to keep radioactive material from spreading. Removing the outer layer of clothing may remove up to ninety percent of radioactive material.
  - Place your contaminated clothing in a plastic bag and seal or tie the bag. Place the bag as far away as possible from

humans and animals so the radiation it gives off does not affect others.

- o Take a shower with a significant amount of soap and water to help remove radioactive contamination. The stronger the flow of water, the better.
- o Do not scrub or scratch the skin.
- o Wash your hair with shampoo or soap and water.
- o Do not use conditioner in your hair because it will bind radioactive material to your hair, keeping it from rinsing out easily.
- o Gently blow your nose and wipe your eyelids and eyelashes with a clean wet cloth. Gently wipe your ears.
- o Make sure to clean your private areas very well.
- o If you cannot shower, use a wipe or clean wet cloth to wipe your skin that was not covered by clothing. Take a shower as soon as possible.

AFTER A NUCLEAR BLAST

Decay rates of the radioactive fallout are the same for any size nuclear device. However, the amount of fallout will vary based on its proximity to the ground. Therefore, it may be necessary for those in the areas with highest radiation levels to shelter for up to a month.

The heaviest fallout would be limited to the area at or downwind from the explosion and eighty percent of the fallout would occur during the first twenty-four hours.

People in most of the areas affected could be allowed to come out of shelter within a few days and, if necessary, evacuate to unaffected areas.

OVERALL DRAWING

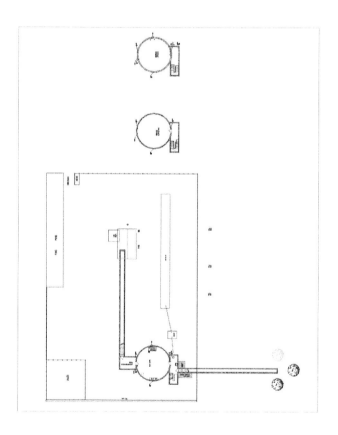

MAIN LEVEL DRAWING

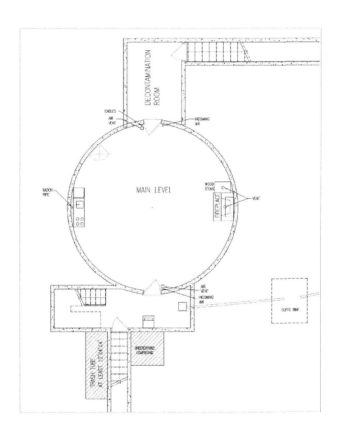

BASEMENT LEVEL DRAWING

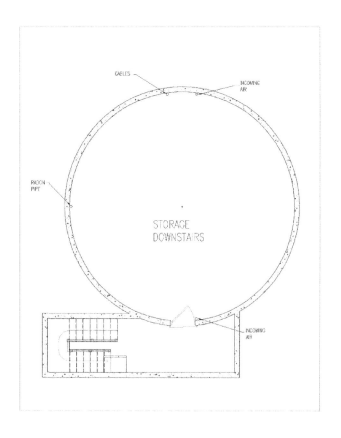

BEDROOM LEVEL DRAWING

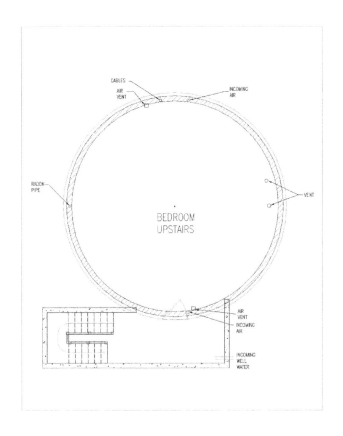

INDEX

QUICK ORDER FORM

 **USE** this form to place an order for additional copies of this or any of our books. Please indicate if you want an eBook or a printed copy. You may also order any of the supplements. Please check the website for the latest books, supplements and prices.

Website	www.doomsdaybunkerbook.com
Email	doomsdaybunkerbook@gmail.com
Fax	855-506-8700
Phone	443-506-8700

Have your credit card ready when calling.
Please send the following Books, eBooks and/or Supplements

QUANTITY	ITEM	PRICE

I understand I may return any item, excluding digital files, for a full refund - for any reason, no questions asked, within seven days of purchase. See our website for FREE information on: Other books, supplements, speaking / seminars, mailing lists, consulting, newsletter and club.

Payment: Visa, MasterCard, Discover, PayPal
Card number:
Name on card: Exp. date: /
Security code

Doomsday Bunker Book

Underground Edition

*Your Complete Guide to
Designing, Surviving and Living
in a Concrete Bunker*

Ben Jakob

Printed in Great Britain
by Amazon

37536026R00136